A dramatic crash in the U.S. Grand Prix West! For more exciting photos of this spectacular incident, turn to page 12.

TIGER ANNUAL 1981

CONTENTS

 85037-583-5

JOHNNY COUGAR

THE PALS WERE GIVEN THEIR INSTRUCTIONS...
JUST TAKE IT EASY FOR THE WARM-UP LAP... THEN ANYTHING GOES!
THAT'S WHAT WORRIES ME!
WAH! YOU TOO FAINT-HEARTED, BILL... JUST FOLLOW SPLASH AND ME...

THEN, AS THEY COMPLETED THE ROLLING LAP...
AND THEY'RE OFF! LOOK AT THEM GO! BILL MACLEAN'S GOT A GOOD START...
YIPPEE! LET'S SEE SOME ACTION!

BILL HAD GOT OVER HIS NERVES...
HEY, THIS ISN'T SO BAD AFTER ALL... I'M GETTING THE HANG OF IT!

BUT JOHNNY WASN'T DOING SO WELL!
WAH! CARS GO MUCH FASTER NOW... VERY CLOSE TOGETHER...

AND...
HEY, LOOK OUT!
HEAP SORRY... CAR NOT GO WHERE COUGAR WANT IT TO!

SPLASH TRIED TO GET PAST HIS PAL, BUT...
HEY, INDIAN MAN... THAT'S REAL MEAN — AAARGH!
COUGAR THINK CAR HAS LIFE OF ITS OWN!

ALL THROUGH THE RACE, JOHNNY WAS INVOLVED IN INCIDENTS...
LOOK AT THAT! COUGAR'S DRIVING LIKE A STOCK-CAR RACER...
SURE MAKES FOR GREAT ACTION, THOUGH!

AT THE FINISH...
FINIS
HURRAH!
BILL MACLEAN **WINS**! A **GREAT** DRIVE... WHICH IS MORE THAN WE CAN SAY FOR HIS FRIEND JOHNNY COUGAR!

SO FAR WE MAKE IT **SIX** CARS HE'S CAUSED TO CRASH... BUT HE'S STILL GOING!

AND HERE COMES COUGAR NOW...AND HE'S LOST IT COMING OUT OF THE FINAL BEND...HE'S SPINNING...

HE'S GONE OVER THE LINE **BACKWARDS**!
FINISH
WELL THAT SURE IS SOME WAY TO FINISH...AND JUDGING BY THE STATE OF HIS CAR, HE WAS LUCKY TO MAKE IT!

IN THE PITS, THE CELEBRITY-CAR MECHANIC COULDN'T BELIEVE HIS EYES!
MY LOVELY CAR— LOOK WHAT YOU'VE **DONE** TO IT, YOU USELESS DRIVER! YOU'D HAVE BEEN BETTER OFF WITH A **TANK**!
HEY, STEADY ON, MAN...

I EXPECT YOU'RE AS USELESS AT WRESTLING AS YOU ARE AT DRIVING, REDSKIN...
WAH, THAT FIGHTING TALK!

IT SURE IS, PAL! I'M QUITE A WRESTLER MYSELF... SO I CHALLENGE YOU TO A CONTEST FOR CHARITY... AND THE LOSER BUYS A NEW CAR!
COUGAR ACCEPT!
WELL THAT'S WHAT WE'RE HERE FOR... I'LL GET THE FIGHT PUT ON AT THE LOCAL HALL...

THE FOLLOWING WEEK...
AND NOW LADIES AND GENTLEMEN, A GRUDGE FIGHT OF SIX ROUNDS, WITH ONE PINFALL OR A KNOCK-OUT TO DECIDE... BETWEEN JOHNNY COUGAR...
GREAT! I NEVER EXPECTED TO SEE JOHNNY WRESTLING HERE!

...AND THE MECHANIC!
HI, FANS... I'LL SOON THROW A SPANNER IN COUGAR'S WORKS!

THE WRESTLERS SHOOK HANDS, AND...
URGH!
OH, SORRY, COUGAR... I'VE JUST DONE AN OIL-CHANGE ON MY PAL'S CAR! HEH, HEH!
CUT THAT OUT, MECHANIC... GET A TOWEL SOMEONE!

AS THE FIGHT STARTED, JOHNNY WENT STRAIGHT INTO ACTION...
YOU WILL NEED MECHANIC TO FIX YOU, BY THE TIME THIS FIGHT OVER!
UHHHH!

BUT AS HIS OPPONENT ROSE FROM THE CANVAS...
NOT BAD... NOW TRY MY **HYDRAULIC JACK** MOVE!
NNNNGG!
WOW! WHAT A HEAD-BUTT... RIGHT UNDER COUGAR'S CHIN!

...AND BEING A MECHANIC, I LIKE WORKING UNDER THINGS, SO...
HE'S GOING FOR A DOUBLE-FOOTED STOMACH THROW...
WATCH OUT, JOHNNY!

LEAVING SO SOON, COUGAR? I HAVEN'T FINISHED SERVICING YOU YET!
AIEEEE!

HOOKAHEY! COUGAR MAKE YOU PAY DEARLY FOR THAT!
LOOK AT THAT! HE'S SOMERSAULTING BACK INTO THE RING!
THE REDSKIN'S REALLY ON THE WARPATH NOW!

BUT AS JOHNNY LANDED IN THE RING...
WAH! WHAT HAPPENED? COUGAR CANNOT MOVE!
HEY, LOOK WHAT THE MECHANIC'S DONE...

...HE GOT AN OLD TYRE FROM HIS CORNER AND THREW IT OVER COUGAR, LIKE A PRIZE AT A HOOPLA STALL!
YOU LOOK A BIT **TYRED**, COUGAR...

...WHY DON'T YOU HAVE A REST?
HEY, CUT THAT FUNNY STUFF OUT, MECHANIC... OR I'LL **DISQUALIFY** YOU!
UUUURGH!

JOHNNY WAS NOT AMUSED!
WAH! COUGAR NOT LIKE BEING MADE TO LOOK STUPID...
ST-STEADY NOW... YOU SHOULDN'T DRIVE YOURSELF TOO HARD, WITH YOUR RADIATOR BOILING LIKE THAT...

WAAAH!
NOTHING WRONG WITH COUGAR'S RADIATOR— BUT YOU ABOUT TO HAVE...

...FLAT BATTERY!
WOW! WHAT A BODY SLAM!
OOOOOOF!

COUGAR'S FOLLOWED THE MOVE DOWN... IT'S A PINFALL POSITION!
YOU LIKE WORKING UNDER THINGS... SO YOU TRY FULL WEIGHT OF COUGAR!
ONE...

YEEEARGH! THIS IS WORSE THAN A TEN-TON TRUCK!
...TWO... **THREE!** THE WINNING PIN-FALL TO JOHNNY COUGAR!
HURRAH! WELL DONE, JOHNNY!

GREAT CONTEST, JOHNNY! YOU SURE GAVE THE MECHANIC THE **WORKS!** HA, HA!
LET'S HAVE A BIG HAND FOR THE WINNER, FOLKS...
YOU MAY HAVE BEATEN ME IN THE RING, REDSKIN — BUT I'D BEAT YOU IN A RACE ON THE TRACK ANY DAY!

WELL, DO YOU ACCEPT MY CHALLENGE TO A CAR RACE?
IF IT IS FOR CHARITY AGAIN... THEN COUGAR ACCEPT!
TERRIFIC! I'M NOT GOING TO MISS SEEING THAT!
NOR ME!

TWO WEEKS LATER, A BIG CROWD WAS AT A LOCAL RACE TRACK TO SEE THE STAR EVENT...
NOW THE RACE YOU'VE ALL BEEN WAITING FOR, FOLKS... JOHNNY COUGAR AGAINST THE MECHANIC IN A TEN LAP, NO-HOLDS-BARRED, DING-DONG!
SEE YOU AT THE FINISH, COUGAR...
YES, I WILL BE THERE FIRST TO GREET YOU!

SECONDS LATER, THEY WERE OFF AND INTO THE FIRST BEND...
THEY'VE HIT ON THE FIRST BEND!
THIS IS GOING TO BE SOME RACE!

JOHNNY'S RIVAL PULLED AHEAD, BUT THE REDSKIN WRESTLER LEFT HIS BRAKING FOR THE NEXT CORNER FAR TOO LATE AND...
COUGAR'S GONE STRAIGHT INTO THE BACK OF THE MECHANIC...
THE MECHANIC CAN'T HOLD IT... HE'S GOING TO SPIN...

IT TOOK TWO LAPS FOR THE MECHANIC TO GET BACK ON TERMS...
AND HERE THEY COME AGAIN, FOLKS! COUGAR LEADS... BUT THE MECHANIC IS LOOKING FOR A WAY THROUGH...
I'LL GET YOU HERE, COUGAR... THEN YOU WON'T SEE ME FOR DUST!

BUT...
COUGAR'S CUT IN TO TRY AND SHUT THE DOOR ON THE MECHANIC... THEY'VE COLLIDED AGAIN!
WOW! THERE'S NOT GOING TO BE MUCH LEFT OF THOSE CARS, BY THE TIME THEY'VE FINISHED!

THEY'VE REBOUNDED FROM THE IMPACT...
THEY'RE HITTING THE SAFETY FENCES ON OPPOSITE SIDES OF THE TRACK...

NOW THEY'VE BOUNCED TOGETHER AGAIN!
AND STILL NO-ONE'S GOT A CLEAR LEAD...

THEN, WHEN BOTH DRIVERS TRIED TO STEER AWAY FROM EACH OTHER...
I CAN'T... TURN THE WHEEL...
NO RESPONSE FROM STEERING...
LOOK! THEIR BUMPERS ARE LOCKED TOGETHER!

AT THE FINISH...
FINIS
IT'S A DEAD-HEAT!
THEY'RE STILL TANGLED TOGETHER... SO NEITHER COULD GET AHEAD OF THE OTHER!

WELL, YOU DIDN'T BEAT ME, COUGAR...
TRUE WORDS, O BIG-MOUTHED ONE— BUT YOU HAVE COME OFF WORSE!
HOW DO YOU MEAN?

NOW YOU HAVE TWO MORE SMASHED UP CARS TO REPAIR!
GAAAH! I JUST CAN'T WIN!

U.S. GRAND PRIX PILE-UP!

Everyone loves to see a motor racing crash—so long as no-one gets hurt! So when one of our top photographers went all the way to Long Beach, California, to cover the U.S. Grand Prix West, he was hoping to bring back some exciting action shots—and he wasn't disappointed, as you can see from the photos on the next four pages.

A peaceful moment at the Long Beach track, before the high-speed action of the race, as mechanics adjust the front 'wings' of Ricardo Patrese's Arrows car. Note the umbrella over the cockpit to keep out the heat of the fierce Californian sun.

A deafening roar of more than 20 highly-tuned racing engines shatters the air, as the race begins, led by the red Ferraris of Gilles Villeneuve, left, and Jody Scheckter.

The cars are tightly-bunched as they go into a right-hand bend, below, and drama is seconds away. Watch car No 5 and the pale blue and white car, behind car 17 on the left.

Suddenly, car No 8, the pale blue and white McLaren driven by Patrick Tambay, starts to mount the rear of car 5, Niki Lauda's Brabham, knocking off its rear wing, above. Now Tambay's car is almost on top of Niki Lauda, below, with the Brabham's rear wing at extreme left, hitting the rear of Jan Lammers' Shadow, disappearing out of photo.

The impact has taken Tambay nearly over Lauda, whose red-topped helmet is centimetres below the flying McLaren. Note Tambay's hands being thrown off the wheel.

After both drivers had got out safely, the wreckage is removed, below. A marshal pushes the remains of Tambay's car off the track, with fuel leaking from underneath.

Meanwhile the race went on, above, with the Ferrari of Canadian ace Gilles Villeneuve leading Nelson Piquet's Brabham into a bend and on the way to a well-deserved victory.

At the end of a gruelling and incident-packed race, the traditional champagne for the popular winner, Gilles Villeneuve, watched by the 2nd place man, Alan Jones.

BILLY'S BOOTS

NOT BAD... BUT A BIT TOO NEAR THE GOAL, JIMMY.
YOU WERE ALWAYS GOING TO GET TO THAT FIRST, REG...

THEY TRIED THE SAME THING AGAIN AND AGAIN...
TOO HIGH... I CAN'T REACH THAT!
THAT'S THE PLACE, THOUGH... IT'S TOO FAR OUT FOR ME TO RUN TO AND PUNCH CLEAR!

UNTIL...
THIS IS THE ONE! IT'S JUST RIGHT!

GOT IT!
GREAT HEADER! THAT'S THE WAY TO DO IT, BILLY!
AAARGH!

THEY PRACTISED EVERY CHANCE THEY HAD... UNTIL THE JUBILEE DAY...
THERE'S GOING TO BE A BIG CROWD WATCHING THE MATCH...
... I HOPE DEAD-SHOT'S OLD BOOTS MAKE ME PLAY WELL...

IT GIVES ME GREAT PLEASURE TO ANNOUNCE THIS SILVER JUBILEE DAY OF GROUNDWOOD SCHOOL... OPEN!
THAT'S JOHN CLOVER... HE'S AN INTERNATIONAL RUNNER. HE WAS IN THE LAST OLYMPICS AND GOT A SILVER MEDAL!
HE USED TO BE A GROUNDWOOD SCHOOL BOY! LET'S GET HIS AUTOGRAPH AFTERWARDS...

DID YOU EVER GET THE CANE WHEN YOU WERE AT GROUNDWOOD, MISTER CLOVER?
NO, I WAS ALWAYS A GOOD BOY!
HE'S A RUNNER, JIMMY... THEY COULDN'T EVER CATCH HIM!

THE SPORTS DAY RACES BEGAN...
STONE ME! GROUNDWOOD COULDN'T FINISH IN THE FIRST TWO! I RECKON YOU CAN RUN FASTER THAN THAT, BILLY!
MAYBE OUR LADS WILL DO BETTER IN THE LONGER RACES.

IN THE HALF-MILE...
HURRRAHHH!
COME ON, GROUNDWOOD!
WE HAVEN'T WON A RACE YET...

BILLY AND JIMMY TOOK PART IN THE RELAY RACE...
OKAY, JIMMY — GO!

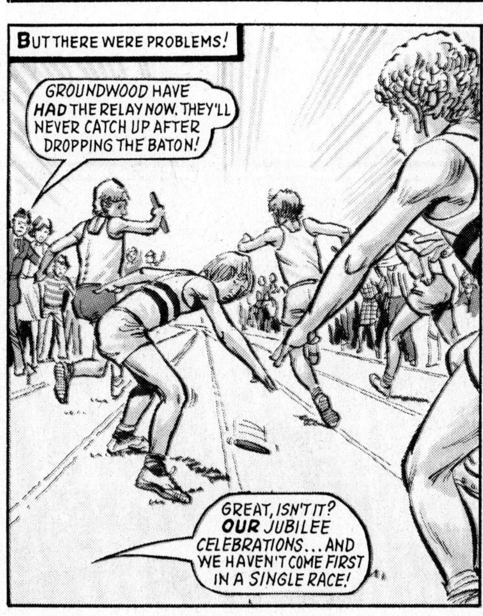
BUT THERE WERE PROBLEMS!
GROUNDWOOD HAVE HAD THE RELAY NOW. THEY'LL NEVER CATCH UP AFTER DROPPING THE BATON!
GREAT, ISN'T IT? OUR JUBILEE CELEBRATIONS... AND WE HAVEN'T COME FIRST IN A SINGLE RACE!

THE FOOTER STARTS IN TWENTY MINUTES. WE'D BETTER GET CHANGED!
MISTER HARRIS DOESN'T LOOK TOO PLEASED...
...I RECKON HE'LL GET THE SACK AS SPORTSMASTER AFTER THIS!

WELL, I HOPE THE FOOTBALL TEAM DOES A BIT BETTER THAN OUR RUNNERS. IT'S UP TO YOU, LADS!
WE'D BETTER WIN SOMETHING HADN'T WE, SIR?

IF WE LOSE... GROUNDWOOD WILL HAVE LOST EVERYTHING TODAY!
WE'VE GOT THE TOUGHEST JOB OF ALL. I MEAN AN ALL-SCHOOLS SIDE HAS GOT TO BE BETTER THAN US!
I JUST HOPE THE OLD BOOTS WORK FOR ME...

THE ALL-SCHOOLS SIDE WAS VERY GOOD...
OH, CRUMBS... HE'S GONE PAST CHARLIE! I HOPE THEY DON'T SCORE IN THE FIRST FEW MINUTES!
10

BUT JIMMY DAWSON CAME ACROSS, AND...
A GOOD TACKLE... HARD BUT FAIR!
GET IT UP THE MIDDLE, JIMMY...

I SHOULD BE UPFIELD... BUT THE OLD BOOTS SEEM TO BE FORCING ME TO HANG BACK...

ALL-SCHOOLS SURGED FORWARD, AND...
HE'S SAVED IT!
NO HE HASN'T ... IT'S STILL GOING TO GO IN!

BUT...
WELL DONE, BILLY! IT'S A GOOD JOB YOU WERE THERE!
THIS IS WHY THE OLD BOOTS MADE ME DROP BACK...

AT HALF-TIME...
WE HAVEN'T DONE BAD, HOLDING THEM TO NIL-NIL. THEY'VE BEEN ALL OVER US!
FAT CHANCE WE'VE HAD OF TRYING OUT OUR FREE-KICK MOVE THAT WE PRACTISED, BILLY...
...WE HAVEN'T BEEN NEAR THEIR END, YET!

FROM THE RE-START...
CRUMBS... I WAS GOING TO DRIBBLE ROUND HIM! IT'S THE OLD BOOTS AGAIN ...THEY SEEMED TO MAKE ME PASS IT!
GREAT BALL, BILLY!

JIMMY RAN ON... ALMOST TO THE PENALTY AREA, WHEN...
PENALTY!
FREE-KICK TO GROUNDWOOD! THAT WAS WELL OUTSIDE THE AREA, LADS!

THIS IS IT, BILLY... ALL THAT PRACTICE WE HAD, MUST PAY OFF!
I'LL GET OVER TO THE FAR SIDE. TAKE THE KICK WHEN I SIGNAL...

THAT'S BILLY'S SIGNAL ...HE'S READY!
WELL, I KNOW WHAT TO DO... I DON'T NEED THE OLD BOOTS TO HELP ME ON THIS ONE...

PERFECT FREE KICK ...JUST RIGHT...

GOOOALLLLL!
IT WORKED! LOVELY GOAL!

ALL-SCHOOLS TRIED DESPERATELY TO GET THE BALL BACK IN THE FEW REMAINING MINUTES, BUT...
OHHHHH!
SMASHING SAVE!
GOOD OLD REG! THEY CAN'T BEAT YOU, CHUM!

THAT WAS IT! GROUNDWOOD SCHOOL'S CUP!
WELL DONE! THAT WAS A GREAT GOAL GROUNDWOOD SCORED, JIMMY!
YES, SIR ... THANKS TO BILLY DANE!

WELL, THE OLD SCHOOL MAY NOT BE PRODUCING GREAT RUNNERS, LIKE THEY HAD IN MY DAY... BUT THEY CAN PLAY FOOTBALL ALL RIGHT!
THANKS, SIR...

WELL DONE, LADS...
GOOD SHOW, GROUNDWOOD!
WELL PLAYED!

IT'S A NICE FEELING TO WIN A CUP, ISN'T IT?
IT'S A NICE FEELING TO HAVE DEAD-SHOT'S OLD BOOTS, TOO!

"**WE should never have come, Skid," growled Sandy McGrath. "It's going to be a shambles."**

"Von Vargen has called a meeting of drivers to try to sort things out," replied Skid Solo. "Personally, I'm all in favour of going ahead. We've still got three days in which to sort everything out, before the race."

Skid Solo, with his mechanic Sandy and a support team, had come to Kaphos, an island in the Aegean Sea, to take part in a round the island road race for works' production model sports cars.

The island was poverty-stricken and backward. Even the best of its roads were so bad that the competitors and their cars were bound to be tested to the limit.

The race was the idea of a multi-millionaire shipping owner named Spardos. He had been born on the island and had left it, penniless, as a young man to seek his fortune. Now he was one of the richest men in the world, but he had never forgotten the hardships of his childhood.

He planned to bring his island birthplace, money, fame and trade by setting up an annual top-class motor racing event, which would attract worldwide interest.

He had recruited top international drivers to compete in the opening race.

"It was a grand idea," Sandy went on, "and yon fellow, Spardos, may know all about the shipping business, and operating oil tankers, but he's a lot to learn about modern motor sport."

Spardos had underestimated the expertise needed to design a course, the organisation needed to control it, the need to be able to foresee and prepare for all the emergencies which would crop up. On top of that, the island, which normally only catered for a handful of tourists, suddenly had to cope with a flood of fans, sightseers, newsmen, TV crews, and traders more eager to cash in.

With only three days to go, it was beginning to look as if the race might never take place. But Skid remained as enthusiastic as when he had first agreed to take part in it, and he was determined to make the drivers who were threatening to pull out, change their minds.

He left the rather delapidated house, where he and Sandy had managed to find cramped and uncomfortable lodgings, and started across the square to the hotel, where most of the other drivers were staying.

At that moment, two men with donkey-carts piled with vegetables entered the square from opposite sides.

They spotted each other, let out yells, and both began lashing their donkeys to a faster pace.

Both were making for a narrow alley that led to the back of the hotel. There was only room for one cart, and neither was going to give way. They collided with a crash. The carts overturned. The donkeys broke loose. Suddenly the square was in an uproar. Fights broke out. Vegetables were used as missiles. A cabbage bounced off Skid's ear, as he made a dash for the hotel entrance. An alarmed doorman let him in, and he stood watching the battle in the square, until whistles blew and the police arrived.

The two who had caused all the trouble were led off shrieking abuse at each other, and within moments everything was back to normal.

"What was all that about?" Skid asked.

The doorman gave a resigned shrug.

"We are used to it. When a man from the village of Noxia meets a man from Limoni, there is always a fight."

"What are they fighting about?"

"Who knows? Who cares? It has been going on for hundreds of years. They have forgotten why they fight."

Skid went on up to Von Vargen's room, where the other top drivers had already gathered.

"Now perhaps we can come to a decision," the German ace said. "We are almost equally divided on whether or not we should cancel our contracts before it is too late."

"I haven't made up my mind yet," said the American, Ken Dale. "I'm waiting to hear what you think, Skid."

"I, too, am of the same position," nodded Toni Mareillia, the Italian ace.

"Right," nodded Skid. "I think Spardos is doing a great thing for Kaphos. To get itself out of this poverty-trap, it needs tourists. But it's no beauty spot, and the weather isn't much attraction. Haven't you noticed? The nights are freezing cold, and in the daytime you can never be sure whether it'll be blistering hot or pouring with rain. This race could put Kaphos on the map, if it becomes a regular event. So let's give it a chance!"

Ken and Toni nodded, others who had been hesitating, joined them.

"You seem to have the majority on your side, Skid," Von Vargen said solemnly.

As the meeting broke up, Ken grinned at Skid.

"You've stuck your neck out, pal," he said. "If this event turns out a fiasco after all, everyone is going to blame you for talking them into it!"

EVENTFUL PRACTICE!

ON each of the two days before the race, all the competitors were allowed to make one practice run over the course.

Skid set off the following morning, with Sandy as his navigator, to get his first real impression of the ordeal that awaited the drivers.

They soon left the small capital town behind and were out into wild, rugged country, dotted with scattered hamlets, each surrounded by a few sparse fields hacked out of the rocky hillside.

Sandy scowled at the map spread out on his lap.

"How am I expected to navigate from this?" he demanded. "It's as out of date as everything else in this backward place."

"I'm afraid so," grinned Skid. "The last survey was done about fifty years ago and it's never been worthwhile to bring it up to date. The people who were born and bred here have never needed maps. But Spardos is having plenty of signs put up."

"You'll never memorise the route in just two trial trips," Sandy warned. "Do you want me to mark in things that are missing off the map?"

"Just the places where there are tall trees alongside the route,"

have come to, according to the official routing instructions, is Limoni. We've gone wrong somewhere!"

"We can't have done," insisted Skid. "We've followed the signs, so we must be right!"

The roar of the car brought people swarming into the street, cheering. Skid was forced to stop. While he was yelling at them to get out of the way, a huge waggon, drawn by a team of powerful horses, and crammed with angry-faced men, thundered into the village.

The cheers of welcome changed to howls of fury. The newcomers went berserk, tearing down the flags and notices, overturning the stalls. The villagers fought back. Skid and Sandy sat trapped in their car while a battle raged round them.

One of the men who had arrived on the waggon, big-muscled, red-faced and with a fierce moustache, clouted his way through the throng to the car and yelled at Skid.

"You have no business here. You have come to the wrong place. You should have come to my village, Limoni. I am the mayor and I will see justice done for my people."

"There must be a misunderstanding. We followed the route signs," protested Skid.

"These dogs from Noxia changed the road signs. They were jealous because we were chosen to be on the route and get a chance to make money, instead of them," yelled the mayor of Limoni.

Skid suddenly remembered the two men fixing the sign to the tree.

By this time, the fighting had died down, and they were joined by a lean and hollow-eyed man, who said he was the mayor of Noxia.

"Listen to me, both of you," Skid said sternly. "Your squabbles aren't my affair, but they will be, if you interfere any more with this race."

He put the car into reverse and drove back the way he had come, until he reached the junction where he had been decoyed off the proper route.

The men from Limoni, having made their protest and feeling that they had taught their ancient rivals from Noxia a lesson, returned to their own village.

Skid instructed.

"The trees?" echoed Sandy, giving him an odd look. "What makes it so important to know where the trees are?"

"The weather," said Skid.

Sandy didn't know what Skid was driving at, but didn't like to admit it.

"Och, yes, of course. The weather," he nodded, looking wise.

Everywhere, frantic preparations were going on to get the course ready in time. Route signs were being put up, straw-bale barriers built, patches of broken road surface mended and potholes filled in.

Each village had been festooned with strings of waving bunting, and with all manner of home-made signs to attract the sightseers to the cakes, wine, fruit, local craftwork and souvenirs offered for sale on tables set up outside every cottage.

The flags, the banners, the posters all helped to distract attention from the official signs and make them more difficult to spot.

They came upon two men nailing a road sign to a tree. The arrow pointed to a steep, winding track which had its surface almost completely crumbled. The men waved their hats and cheered as Skid bounced by in a cloud of dust.

Sandy stared into his lap.

"This map is useless. This road isn't even marked on it. I'm getting lost."

They splashed through a ford. The road surface on the other side became worn, ancient cobblestones, and led them into a village, with a huge banner stretched across the street which read: "Welcome to Noxia."

"That's funny," frowned Sandy. "Noxia isn't even on the map. The next place we should

The following morning, they were all out in the main street, waiting for the cars to come through on their second practice run. Excitement rose when they heard the whine of engines in the distance. But though they waited, nothing arrived. The sounds faded away again.

The mayor scowled in dark suspicion.

"Come," he growled.

All the men in the village followed him in a body until, at a road junction, they came in sight of a barrier of barrels.

On the other side of the barrier, Skid, with his map, was arguing with the mayor of Noxia.

Even while they stood and argued, more carts loaded with barrels were coming up from Noxia, to make the barrier even more solid.

Von Vargen had stopped, and was listening, his face as black as thunder. At that moment, Ken Dale arrived, pulled up his car, and came to find out what was happening.

It was clear enough. The people of Noxia had decided that if the race wasn't to go through their village, it shouldn't go through Limoni either, so they were building a barrier to force the cars to by-pass it.

The men from Limoni charged, and began to tear down the barrels, scattering them all over the road. As fast as they did so, the men from Noxia rescued them and started to put them back.

Von Vargen yelled at Skid to make himself heard above the din.

"This is all your fault. These stupid peasants will not allow the race to take place. You should not have made us change our minds."

"I'm afraid he's right, Skid," agreed Ken Dale. "I'm going back to start packing up. I'm pulling out, and I guess most of the other drivers will, too."

"No, wait," begged Skid. "We'll go and see Spardos. Bring these two stubborn mayors along."

Back in town, in Spardos' office, the two rivals screamed at each other, neither prepared to give way. Spardos himself was in despair. The project had been the dream of his life. But he had reckoned without the centuries-old feud between Noxia and Limoni. In spite of all that he had invested in it, he was prepared to cut his losses and call the whole thing off.

Skid had to wait impatiently for a chance to get a word in.

"Listen!" he managed at last. "Why can't you re-route the race so that it goes through both places?"

"There is only one direct through road, and it is very bad, because nobody in either village will embark on a journey which would take him through the other," groaned Spardos. "Besides, there is the bridge. It is so unsafe, even the children are not allowed to play on it."

"Let's go and see," said Skid.

Midway between the two villages, the road was carried by an ancient wooden, trestle bridge. Over the years, bits had been allowed to fall off it. It certainly didn't look as if it would take the weight of a succession of speeding cars.

Skid clambered on to it and inspected it carefully.

"It's not so bad as it looks," he declared. "I'm sure it could be made safe. How soon can we start work on it? Who will we get to repair it?"

"It is our bridge. We will repair it," said the mayor of Noxia.

"No. It is our bridge. We will mend it," countered the mayor of Limoni.

"Don't start that again," begged Skid. "You'll just have to forget your feud for once, get together, and figure out a way to share the job."

The two mayors reacted with horror, as if the very idea was unthinkable.

"Explain one thing to me. Why is it that when a man from Noxia meets a man from Limoni, they always fight?" asked Skid.

"Because it has always been so," both said together.

"But what are they fighting *about?*"

The two men stared at each other, dumb. Neither knew the answer. They had never really stopped to think about it.

"Are you going to let this spoil the only chance you'll ever get of making both your villages prosperous?" taunted Skid.

The two men continued to stare at each other. Both were convinced by Skid's words, but neither wanted to show weakness by making the first move. Skid decided it for them, by grabbing each by the right wrist and pulling their hands together.

"You'd better shake on it, then go away and get yourselves sorted out. There's a lot to do, and not much time."

The two men went out together, vague-eyed, as if they still didn't know what had hit them.

Skid turned to grin at Spardos and the others.

"I think it is going to be all right," he promised.

A TOUGH RACE!

THE following morning, the square was packed with spectators for the start of the race.

Skid eased himself behind the wheel of his car and was joined by Sandy.

"What sort of night was it?" asked Skid.

"I hardly slept a wink," growled Sandy.

"I mean the temperature."

"It must have been the coldest since we arrived. The water was frozen in my jug," the Scottish mechanic replied.

"And the forecast?"

"A short spell of heavy rain. Then hot sun."

Skid nodded thoughtfully.

"Don't forget to warn me when we are coming to trees," he reminded Sandy.

The massed start in the square, was a snarling, dog-fighting scrimmage to secure a good position. Most of the drivers had decided

that the best tactics were to try to get out in front and stay there.

Skid took no part in the scramble. His plan was the opposite. He was convinced that steady caution would be the trump card, and that the over-eager ones would wreck themselves long before they completed the circuit.

He was proved right. A few miles from the start, as they approached a bend, Sandy said for the first time: "Trees!"

Skid checked his speed and steadied the car. As he went though the bend he felt the tail start to slide under him, but he kept control.

When he came through at the other end, he saw a glum driver standing, shoulders hunched in dejection, beside a car that was almost hidden in steam.

From then on, the road became littered with breakdowns.

As Sandy had predicted, after a short sharp spell of heavy rain, the sun began to blaze hotly.

They were approaching Noxia. Toni Mareillia was ahead of them. The ford still had thin ice floating on it as he went through.

"Trees!" warned Sandy again.

The Italian, anxious not to let Skid overtake him before they reached the cobbled, narrow village street, revved his engine hard, and overdid it. He was caught by surprise when the surge of power pushed his car into an uncontrollable skid, which caused it to spin round twice before going backwards off the road and ramming a rotting wooden fence, which collapsed.

If Skid hadn't been anticipating something of the sort, he could have been into the back of his rival and the results might have been nasty, but he had been prepared for possible trouble, and thundered by in safety.

The road beyond the village was flat and without shade. The sun blazed down, but the road was still awash from the heavy rain, and the water concealed the unevenness of the surface.

Yet another driver in trouble ahead proved to be Ken Dale, who had bounced out of an unseen pothole and broken a half-shaft.

Sandy, keeping a check on the drivers they had passed, said: "I think we've only got Von Vargen in front of us now".

There was no sign of the German driver when they came in sight of the bridge, which was swarming with people; not on it, but underneath it, watching for any signs of weakness as they sat astride the trestle supports, which shook noisily as each car roared over the timber span.

They were on a long straight stretch, when they came in sight of Von Vargen.

"We're gaining on him," declared Sandy.

"But not fast enough to catch him, unless he makes a mistake," said Skid.

Von Vargen was so experienced, that he rarely made mistakes. But he did this time.

He was approaching a bend that led to a cluster of cottages at the end of the straight, when he caught sight of Skid in his rear view mirror.

He was so surprised, that he momentarily lost his concentration and instinctively turned his head to look back.

It was an expensive lapse.

It took him only a split second to realise what he was doing, but by then it was too late. The car had covered a lot of ground in the brief interval before he brought his eyes back to the road.

He was rushing at the bend, and right ahead of him was a barrier of straw bales blocking off a side road.

He had no time to swerve. He went straight through them.

He didn't hurt himself, or his car, but he created a terrible mess, and by the time he had reversed out of it, Skid was by and building up a lead which he hung on to without trouble until he crossed the finishing line in the town square.

Thanks to Skid, the race had turned out a sensational success, even though half the competitors failed to finish. All the most spectacular bits had been captured by the TV cameras and would be screened to thrill fans all over the world.

Spardos was effusive in his thanks to Skid for what he had done for Kaphos, not only for putting it on the way to becoming a road-racing centre, but for bringing peace to the island by settling the centuries-old feud.

But Sandy was still bothered.

"Why did I have to keep telling you about trees?" he asked.

"To warn me of sudden changes in the road surface of course," grinned Skid. "The bitterly cold nights produce thick frost and ice. Then the sun comes up and melts the frost, but not in the heavy shade under the trees, where the road may stay hard and treacherous for hours if you're not prepared for it. You saw what happened. It caught a lot of people by surprise. But we were ready for it!"

"Och! Ye're a canny mon, Skid!" grinned the happy Scot. "I suppose I couldna see the wood for the trees!"

The Choice of CHAM

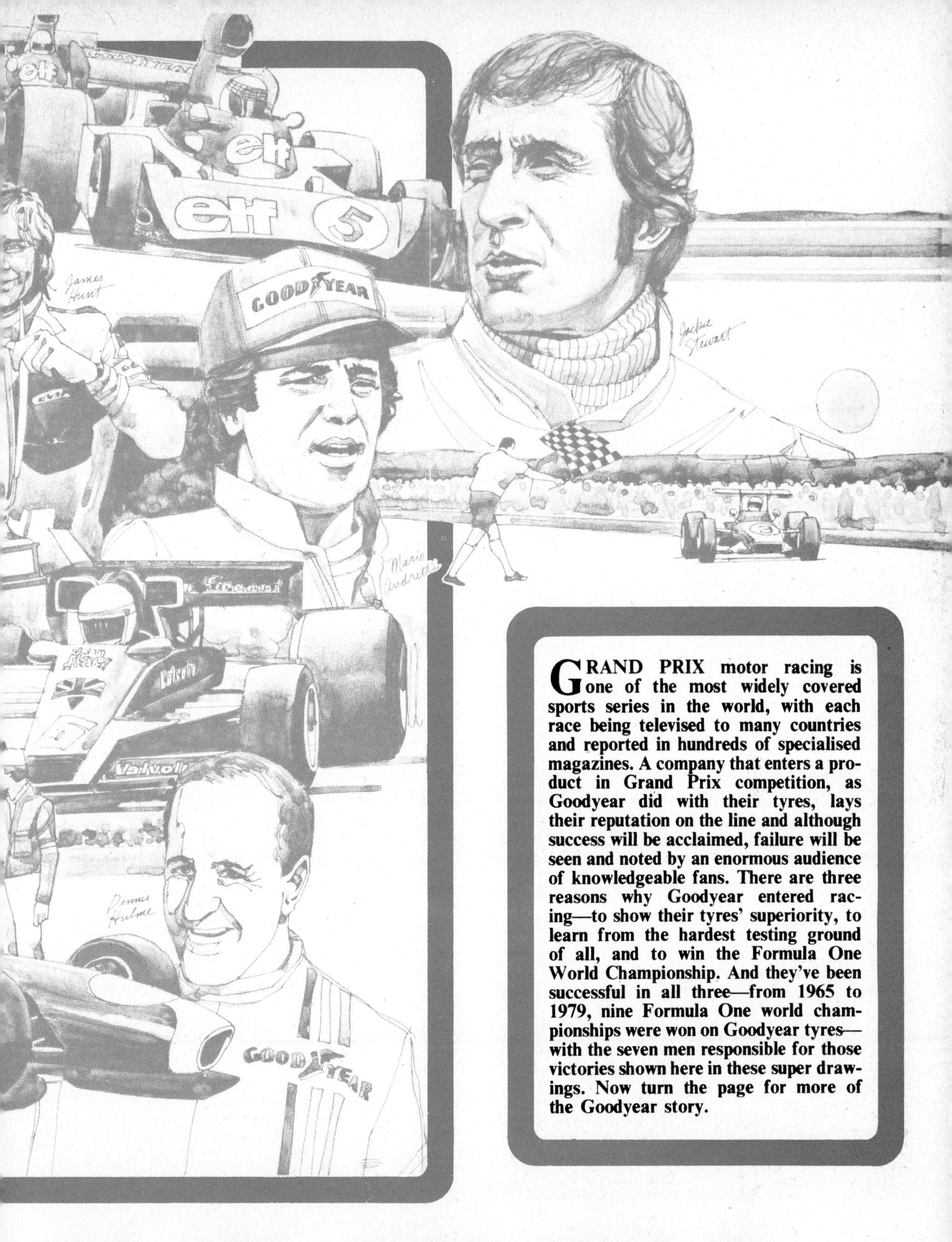

GRAND PRIX motor racing is one of the most widely covered sports series in the world, with each race being televised to many countries and reported in hundreds of specialised magazines. A company that enters a product in Grand Prix competition, as Goodyear did with their tyres, lays their reputation on the line and although success will be acclaimed, failure will be seen and noted by an enormous audience of knowledgeable fans. There are three reasons why Goodyear entered racing—to show their tyres' superiority, to learn from the hardest testing ground of all, and to win the Formula One World Championship. And they've been successful in all three—from 1965 to 1979, nine Formula One world championships were won on Goodyear tyres—with the seven men responsible for those victories shown here in these super drawings. Now turn the page for more of the Goodyear story.

PIONS!

Goodyear completed their first full season in Formula One in 1965. Then, in 1966, the great Australian driver Jack Brabham, above, brought them their first world championship, and a "first" for himself as well, being the first driver to win the championship in a car of his own design-the Brabham-Repco V8.

The famous tyre company didn't have to wait long for their next world championship win. For, in 1967, New Zealander Denny Hulme, above—Jack Brabham's number two driver—changed places with his boss, winning the Formula One title, with Jack second!

The way racing tyres have evolved over the years is illustrated in the chart on the right. Whereas the 1966 tyre had a tread width of 9.5 inches on a 15 inch diameter wheel, the 1972 tyre had a two inch smaller wheel, but a tyre width of 14.1 inches—the modern low profile tyre, which gives maximum grip and has subsequently been applied to ordinary road tyres.

GOODYEAR

RACE TYRE EVOLUTIO

1966
9·5" T.W. 15" RIM
ASPECT RATIO 60%

1969
13·0" T.W. 15" RIM

1967
11·5" T.W. 15" RIM

1970
1971
13·1" T.W. 13" RIM

1968
12·0" T.W. 15" RIM

1972
14·1" T.W. 13" RIM
ASPECT RATIO 30%

The rubber outer casing of Goodyear tyres is manufactured to very high standards, right, as are the number of components that go to build a product that has to be totally relied upon by its user. A faulty tyre could result in death or serious injury.

From Hulme's victory in 1967, Goodyear had to wait until 1971 for their next world championship win, by Jackie Stewart, in a Tyrrell, below. But the "Flying Scotsman" gave them good value for money—by winning the title again in 1973!

Another "double" Goodyear Formula One world champion was the courageous Austrian, Niki Lauda, right. After winning in 1975 at the wheel of his Ferrari, he nearly died in a 1976 crash at Hockenheim, but recovered to incredibly take the world title again in 1977!

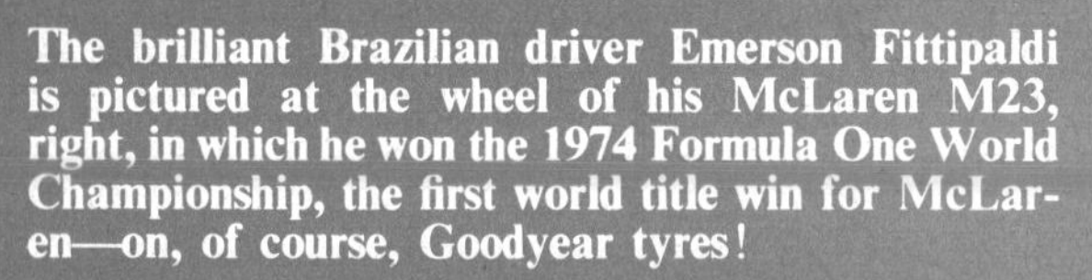

The brilliant Brazilian driver Emerson Fittipaldi is pictured at the wheel of his McLaren M23, right, in which he won the 1974 Formula One World Championship, the first world title win for McLaren—on, of course, Goodyear tyres!

All racing tyres used to have a "tread" pattern cut into them, until the appearance of the 'slick' tyre, left, which is completely smooth and relies on a heat build-up to enable it to 'stick' to the track in dry conditions, giving much faster speeds. Mario Andretti, below left, gave Goodyear their 9th Formula One world championship, when he drove his Lotus to a record six Grand Prix victories in 1978, to win the title by a huge margin. Finally, the first Englishman to win the world championship since Graham Hill in 1968—James Hunt, below, in his Marlboro McLaren. In the final race of the 1976 series, James thought he had lost the title through a slow tyre change, then discovered he had in fact won—by a single point. Goodyear had done it again.

THE RECORD BREAKER!

THEY say life begins at 40, and how true that was for New Zealander Ivan Mauger, when he won his record-breaking 6th Speedway World Final on September 2nd, 1979—one month before his fortieth birthday! 16 riders from ten countries, converged on Chorzow in Poland, to battle for the title. Each rider competed in five, four-lap races, with three points being awarded for a win, two points for second and one for third. Mauger was in devastating form, winning four races and finishing second in the other, to beat the record of five World Final wins, he shared with the great Ove Fundin. You can see some action from that historic final on the next few pages.

A great moment for young American rider Kelly Moran, as he stands in front of his country's flag, above, at the opening ceremony of the 1979 World Final, watched by over 100,000 fans in the vast Slaski stadium. It was Kelly's first Final, but he was soon in the thick of the action, below, battling with Poland's Zenon Plech, No. 7. The 18-year-old American rode brilliantly, to finish fourth overall.

England's three hopes for honours at Chorzow, above, were Dave Jessop (left), Mike Lee (centre), who both ride for King's Lynn and Peter Collins, Belle Vue. Peter was Britain's last world champion, winning in 1976 and he started the 1979 Final as favourite. But Mike Lee, seen in centre of Mauger and Jancarz, below, achieved our best position, finishing 3rd, the only rider to win a race off Mauger.

Runner-up in the Final was Zenon Plech of Poland and Hackney, who delighted his home supporters with some great riding. Here, above, he leads from his fellow countryman Edward Jancarz, left, and British Champion, Peter Collins. One extra race was to decide 3rd place, and it went to England's Mike Lee, left below, getting ahead as Kelly Moran does a "wheelie" and Billy Sanders cuts across 3-times world champ, Ole Olsen.

Heat 17, Ivan Mauger's fifth and last race—and after twice bumping the tapes at the start, the New Zealander roared to the front, above, ahead of Britain's Peter Collins and 1978 champion, Ole Olsen of Denmark. Below, Mauger is out on his own and riding to win. 72.8 seconds after the start, he hurtled across the finishing line to become 1979 World Champion! His victory came at a time when other riders would have been thinking of retiring!

The track is silent; gone are the snarling speedway machines, but the massive crowd makes more noise than a thousand speedway bikes as it acclaims the greatest speedway rider the world has ever known. Proudly, Ivan Mauger holds aloft the number six, left, to show the fans that he has won a record six World Individual Speedway titles—1968, 1969, 1970, 1972, 1977 and now 1979!

Victory is sweet, right, as Ivan stands on top of the winner's rostrum, with his wife Raye Mauger, flanked by second place man Zenon Plech, right, and Britain's Mike Lee, left. The rider seated in front is American Kelly Moran, savouring the triumphant moment of coming fourth in his first World Final—at the ripe old age of 18! Could he become the Ivan Mauger of the future?

HOT-SHOT HAMISH!
HAMISH BALFOUR WAS BROUGHT FROM A SMALL HEBRIDEAN ISLAND TO PLAY SOCCER FOR PRINCES PARK, A CLUB IN THE SCOTTISH LEAGUE. PRINCES HAD A HARD SEASON AND TOWARDS THE END, THEY BATTLED FOR PRECIOUS POINTS AGAINST MULLFORD RANGERS. HAMISH HAD THE BALL... AND HE TRIED HIS FAMOUS SHOT!
WHAT'S THE MATTER, HAMISH? CAN YE NO' SHOOT STRAIGHT? YE USED TO BE THE BEST SHOT IN THE GAME!
THE HOT-SHOT!
HE'S HIT THE BAR!

GNNNJURRR!
HE'S GOT HIS OWN BACK!
SO HAS THE BALL!

THE NEXT TIME HAMISH KICKED A FOOTBALL... WAS ON HIS ISLAND HOME.
THAT'S IT, SON! NICE SHOT! YE'VE HIT THE TARGET... NOW THE NEXT ONE!
OCH, AWAY, DADDIE... THIS IS AWFUL HARD WORK!

FASTER, MON! WHAT ARE YE HANGING ABOOT FOR?
I CANNA GO ANY FASTER, DADDIE!

YE HAD NO RIGHT TO ENTER ME IN A SHARP-SHOOTING CONTEST, ANYWAY! NOT WITHOUT ASKING ME...
THERE WAS A PRIZE OF FIVE HUNDRED POUNDS, HAMISH. I COULDNA' RESIST IT...

BUT THE SHARP-SHOOTING IS WITH GUNS! NOT FOOTBALLS!
AYE. BUT I DIDNA KEN THAT AT THE TIME, LADDIE...
SHARP-SHOOTING COMPETITION

IT'S HOPELESS, DADDIE. IT TAKES ME TEN TIMES AS LONG TO KICK FOOTBALLS AT THE TARGETS AS IT DOES FOR A MON TO SHOOT BULLETS AT THEM. I CANNA WIN!
MAYBE I CAN ENTER YE FOR SOMETHING ELSE. THERE'S LOTS OF COMPETITIONS IN THE ISLAND GAMES...

WELL, I'LL LEAVE YE TO THINK IT OOT, DADDIE... I'M GOING FOR A WALK ON THE BEACH...
THAT'S IT, LADDIE. I'LL DO ALL THE BRAIN-WORK...

OCH, IF IT ISN'T HAMISH BALFOUR! I USED TO TEACH YE FISHING AS A LADDIE... DO YE REMEMBER?
AYE, I RECALL IT WELL, ANGUS. NICE TO SEE YE AGAIN...

HAMISH EXPLAINED TO ANGUS HIS TROUBLE WITH THE 'SHARP-SHOOTING' CONTEST...
THE TROUBLE IS, ANGUS... I CANNA KICK FAST ENOUGH!
YOU'RE GOING ABOUT IT THE WRONG WAY, LADDIE. USE YERE HEAD, MON!

I COULDNA USE MY HEAD, ANGUS... I COULDN'T HEAD THE BALL AS FAR AS THAT! THE TARGETS ARE TWENTY-FIVE METRES AWAY!
I MEANT YE SHOULD USE YERE BRAINS... YE NINNY!

HAMISH TROTTED AWAY... AND CAME BACK WITH SIX FOOTBALLS...
I RUN UP AND KICK THE FIRST BALL, ANGUS... AND BY THE TIME I RUN BACK TO KICK THE SECOND... THE CHAP WITH THE REVOLVER'S ALREADY FIRED AT LEAST TWICE!
YE HAVENA GOT A SINGLE CLUE IN YERE FAT HEAD, HAVE YE? COME HERE, MON... AND I'LL SHOW YE THE PROPER WAY!

HAMISH DID WHAT ANGUS TOLD HIM, AND...
SEE! IT'S MUCH QUICKER THAT WAY, EH? NOW YE JUST SPEED THAT UP... AND YE'RE IN WITH A CHANCE!
ANGUS, YE'RE A WEE GENIUS!

LATER...
DADDIE, I'VE FOUND A WAY TO KICK TEN TIMES FASTER! MAYBE I'LL WIN THE SHARP-SHOOTERING EVENT AFTER ALL!
THAT'S GOOD. PERHAPS WE'LL WIN ONE **THOUSAND** POUNDS, TOO... BECAUSE I'VE ENTERED YE IN THE ROWING RACE. YE'RE STRENGTH WILL TELL THERE, LADDIE!

HAMISH WAS LED TO A ROWING BOAT...
HURRY UP, SON... WE'VE TIME FOR A WEE BIT OF PRACTICE.
I'M HUNGRY, DADDIE! IT'S PAST MY TEA-TIME...

NOW I WANT TO SEE YE GET AWAY TO A **FAST** START, LADDIE! A SECOND SAVED AT THE **BEGINNING** OF THE RACE... CAN BE **VITAL** AT THE **END**!
I KNOW THAT, DADDIE... IT'S COMMONSENSE!

THREE—TWO—ONE... **GO**!
ARRRRRRGHHHH!

YE NEED STRONGER OARS, MON! I'LL MAKE YE SOME!
AYE, STRONGER OARS... AND A CRASH-HELMET! I WHACKED MY HEAD!

NOW TWO OF THOSE WOULD MAKE OARS THAT EVEN HAMISH COULDNA' BREAK!

IF THAT SON OF MINE BREAKS THESE... I'LL HIT HIM OVER THE HEAD WITH THEM!

I'VE GOT THE THINGS YE NEED, LADDIE! STAND UP AND TAKE THEM!
AYE, THEY LOOK STRONG ENOUGH, DADDIE...

HAVE YE GOT THEM, SON?
AYE, I'VE GOT THEM...

WHERE'S THE ROWING-BOAT?
IT'S SUNK, DADDIE... THE NEW OARS ARE TOO HEAVY!

THEY DECIDED NOT TO ENTER THE ROWING-BOAT RACE. ON THE DAY OF THE ISLAND GAMES...
ISLAND GAMES
TO-DAY!!
EVERYONE ENJOY THE FUN! SEE THE
RACING
SHOOTING
ROWING
RUNNING
and all the fun of the Fair!
ALL WELCOME!
20 pence TO GET IN!
THE SHARP-SHOOTING WAS A GREAT ATTRACTION...
YE'RE NO GOOD, DUNCAN McBATT. YE CANNA SHOOT FOR TOFFEE!
THERE'S ONLY ONE MON GOT SIX BULLS-EYES, HAMISH. BUT HE WAS SLOW! YOU CAN WIN!
AYE. BUT I'LL STILL HAVE TO MOVE FAST!
THEN IT WAS HAMISH'S TURN...
WHAT ARE YE DOING, YE NINNY? YE'VE GOT TO HIT ALL THE TARGETS... NOT JUST ONE!
AYE. AND I CAN DO IT THIS WAY... AND QUICKER! ANGUS McFISH TAUGHT ME!
HAMISH RAN AT THE LINE OF BALLS. AND...
OCH, THAT'S BRILLIANT ENOUGH FOR ME TO HAVE THOUGHT UP!

SIX BULLS IN SIX SHOTS... IN SIX SECONDS! HAMISH IS THE WINNER!
YE DID IT, HAMISH!
I'LL SAY IT MYSELF! THAT WAS PRETTY GOOD GOING, DADDIE!
I CROWN YE, HAMISH BALFOUR... KING OF THE ISLAND GAMES!
THAT'S MY BOY!
I FEEL KIND OF DAZED WITH IT ALL...

I-I FEEL KINDA DAZED WITH IT ALL!
HE'S COMING ROUND!
THE BALL FETCHED HIM AN AWFUL HARD CRACK!

WHAT—WHAT HAPPENED? I THOUGHT I WAS AT MY ISLAND HOME, WITH MY DADDIE...
YE WERE LAID OOT, HAMISH! YE'VE BEEN UNCONSCIOUS ALMOST FIVE MINUTES. YE'D BETTER COME OFF...THERE'S NO' A LONG TO GO, ANYWAY...

WE WON, HAMISH...THREE-ONE!
THERE'S A PHONE CALL FOR YE, HAMISH...IT'S YERE DADDIE ON THE LINE!
MY DADDIE? WHAT DOES HE WANT?

IS THAT YE, HAMISH? I WAS WONDERING IF YE CAN GET HOME FOR A FEW DAYS? WE'VE GOT THE ISLAND GAMES STARTING HERE AND I THINK YE COULD WIN A FEW THINGS...

I'LL BE THERE, DADDIE! I'D LIKE TO ENTER THE SHARP-SHOOTING CONTEST...
SHARP-SHOOTING? YE'RE MAD! YE CANNA FIRE A GUN TO SAVE YERE LIFE!

I'VE THOUGHT OF A WAY I COULD WIN BY KICKING FOOTBALLS AT THE TARGETS, DADDIE...
FOOTBALLS? YE'RE OFF YERE HEAD! YE'LL NEVER WIN!

NO, I CAN DO IT, DADDIE...IT CAME TO ME IN A DREAM! YE'LL SEE WHEN I GET THERE!

The SLOGGER from DOWN UNDER

COP THAT, SPORTS! IT'S THE WINNING HITOR I'M A CROSS-EYED WALLABY!

DIGGER DEAN WAS MAD ON CRICKET. ALTHOUGH HE RAN A CATTLE STATION IN THE REMOTE OUTBACK OF AUSTRALIA, HE MANAGED TO KEEP HIS EYE IN BY ORGANISING SCRATCH GAMES WHENEVER HE COULD, WITH THE HELP OF STATION HANDS AND NEIGHBOURS . . .

AND SO . . .

AT DEAN TOWERS, DIGGER'S EXPECTED ARRIVAL COINCIDED WITH THE ANNUAL CRICKET MATCH BETWEEN A GUEST TEAM OF COUNTY CLUB MEMBERS AND A FIFTEEN-MAN SIDE OF ESTATE TENANTS . . .
WHAT'S YOUR COUSIN CEDRIC LIKE, CLARENCE?
THAT PORTRAIT WAS PAINTED JUST BEFORE HE WAS TAKEN TO AUSTRALIA AS A BOY.
HE LOOKS VERY REFINED AND PROPER — A TYPICAL DEAN.
I UNDERSTAND CEDRIC HAS PLAYED A LOT OF CRICKET IN AUSTRALIA. HE SHOULD BE A REAL HELP TO THE COUNTY IN KEEPING THE CUP THIS SEASON.
I SAY, CLARENCE, YOU'VE GOT A MOST ODD-LOOKING VISITOR!
HI! I'M DIGGER DEAN AND THIS IS MY MATE — JIM-JIM. YOU MUST BE COUSIN CLARENCE. PUT IT THERE!
THERE MUST BE SOME MISTAKE. YOU— YOU CAN'T POSSIBLY BE THE PERSON WE'RE EXPECTING!
DIGGER WAS EAGER TO SEE WHAT HE HAD INHERITED . . .
SOME LAY-OUT, SPORT. I SUPPOSE THESE ARE THE DUDS WE WEAR ON SPECIAL OCCASIONS!
PLEASE DON'T TOUCH!
WHY NOT? DON'T THEY BELONG TO US?
HEY, SPORT! BOWL ME ONE OF THOSE MELONS AND SEE ME KNOCK IT FOR SIX!
WHO, SIR? ME, SIR?
THIS IS IMPOSSIBLE!
WELL, MATE, WHAT ABOUT THIS CRICKET MATCH? HOW SOON DO WE START?
WE WOULDN'T HAVE A LOUT LIKE YOU IN OUR TEAM! YOU CAN'T POSSIBLY BE A DEAN. YOU'RE A FRAUD — AN IMPOSTOR—!
PULL YOUR NECK IN, MATE. I'M CEDRIC DEAN AND I CAN PROVE IT. BUT I GET THE MESSAGE. I'M NOT GOOD ENOUGH TO MIX WITH YOU TOFFEE-NOSED DRONGOES. SO JIM-JIM AND I WILL PLAY FOR THE OTHER TEAM!
DO YOU WISH ME TO SUMMON THE — AH — CONSTABULARY, SIR?
CERTAINLY NOT, PERKINS. WE CAN'T HAVE A SCANDAL. FOR THE MOMENT WE MUST LET THIS ROUGHNECK HAVE HIS WAY. HE SEEMS TO IMAGINE HE CAN PLAY CRICKET. IF WE MAKE HIM LOOK FOOLISH, PERHAPS HE'LL GO AWAY.
CLARENCE WON THE TOSS AND DECIDED TO PUT HIMSELF IN FIRST. DIGGER WAS TO OPEN THE BOWLING . . .
GO FOR HIM, CLARENCE!
KNOCK THE COVER OFF THE BALL!

BUT CLARENCE HAD NO CHANCE!
HE'S OUT FIRST BALL!
HE WAS BEATEN ALL ENDS UP!
THE NEXT MAN DECIDED TO PLAY HIMSELF IN, BEFORE ATTEMPTING ANY SCORING STROKES. BUT WHEN HE TRIED TO BREAK HIS DUCK . . .
HE'S OUT!
WHAT A CATCH!
DESPITE THEIR BAD START, THE COUNTY SIDE WERE ABLE TO SCORE 150. THEN IT WAS TIME FOR DIGGER AND JIM-JIM, WATCHED SCORNFULLY BY THE SOUTHSHIRE PLAYERS, TO OPEN THEIR INNINGS . . .
THEY DRAW STUMPS AT SEVEN O'CLOCK, BOSS. WE'LL HAVE TO GO SOME.
TOO RIGHT, COBBER. THOSE DRONGOES DIDN'T LEAVE US MUCH TIME.
CLARENCE PUT HIMSELF ON TO OPEN THE BOWLING, DETERMINED TO GET HIS REVENGE . . .
CRACK!
SIX OFF THE FIRST BALL!
IT MUST BE A FLUKE!
DIGGER AND JIM-JIM CONTINUED TO CLOUT THE BALL ALL OVER THE FIELD, EVEN AFTER CLARENCE HAD TAKEN HIMSELF OFF . . .
YOUR COUSIN MAY BE A BIT OF A ROUGH DIAMOND, BUT HE KNOWS HIS CRICKET! I THINK YOU OUGHT TO MAKE FRIENDS WITH HIM . . .
NEVER. IF HE'S GENUINE, HE'S A DISGRACE TO THE FAMILY. I'M MAKING IT MY BUSINESS TO SEE THAT HE GOES BACK TO HIS SMELLY SHEEP-FARM, THE SOONER THE BETTER.
FOUR MORE. YOU NEEDN'T HAVE BOTHERED TO PUT YOUR PADS ON, JACK.
AYE, AND COUNTY SIDE NEEDN'T HAVE ALLOWED US FIFTEEN BATSMEN! T'OTHER THIRTEEN COULD HAVE GONE HOME AT TEA-TIME . . !
BUT SOON IT WAS BECOMING A BATTLE AGAINST THE CLOCK . . .
THIS MUST BE THE LAST BALL. THERE WON'T BE TIME FOR ANOTHER OVER.
IT'S THE AUSSIE'S LAST CHANCE TO MAKE THE WINNING STROKE. HE'S GOT TO HIT THE BALL FOR SIX. CAN HE DO IT?

THE AUSSIE HAS GOT TO CLOUT THIS ONE OVER THE BOUNDARY!
CLARENCE IS MOVING EVERYONE DEEP TO TRY FOR A CATCH.

DIGGER'S WELL-WORN, BRASS-BOUND BAT MET THE BALL WITH A SMACK THAT COULD BE HEARD FOR MILES.
SMACK!

IT WAS THE MOST TREMENDOUS HIT EVER SEEN ON THE GROUND!
KER-RASH!
THE WINNING HIT! AND WHAT A HIT- HE'S SMASHED THE CLOCK!
NO-ONE HAS EVER DRIVEN A BALL SO FAR OUT OF THE GROUND BEFORE!

CONGRATULATIONS! THAT WAS A SPLENDID KNOCK!
THANKS, SPORT. THOSE ARE THE FIRST KIND WORDS I'VE HAD FROM YOUR MOB SINCE I GOT HERE!

DIGGER LOOKED AT HIS COUSIN, BUT CLARENCE HAD TURNED HIS BACK TO HIDE HIS DISAPPOINTMENT.
CLARENCE IS A SNOB. SO ARE MOST OF THE COUNTY TEAM. YOU'LL HAVE A PACKET OF TROUBLE WITH HIM, IF YOU INTEND TO STAY HERE!
TOO RIGHT I'M STAYING, COBBER- AT LEAST UNTIL THE END OF THE CRICKET SEASON!

NEVER THOUGHT I'D LIVE TO SEE THE DAY. WE'VE PLAYED THIS MATCH EVERY YEAR SINCE I WAS A BOY. THIS IS THE FIRST TIME WE EVER BEAT THE COUNTY!
BEST OF IT IS, THEY WERE GOING TO LET US HAVE FIFTEEN BATSMEN ON OUR SIDE, BUT WE ONLY NEEDED TWO!

THAT'S IT THEN UNTIL NEXT YEAR. BEST BE OFF HOME.
WAIT. YOU CAN'T GO HOME YET, THERE'S A BIG NOSH-UP LAID OUT IN THE HOUSE. FOLLOW ME.

PARDON ME, SIR. BUT THE REFRESHMENTS ARE FOR THE HOUSE GUESTS. THERE ARE MEAT-PASTE SANDWICHES AND LEMONADE FOR THE LOCAL PEOPLE IN THE MARQUEE ON THE LAWN.
COP THIS, SPORT! THESE ARE MY MATES! CLARENCE AND HIS MOB DON'T WANT TO KNOW ME. WHERE I EAT—MY MATES EAT... UNDERSTOOD?
Y-YES, SIR.
YOUR COUSIN'S A GREAT CHARACTER. I LIKE HIM. AND WE COULD REALLY DO WITH HIS BATTING IF SOUTHSHIRE ARE TO KEEP THE CHALLENGE CUP THIS YEAR...
UNTHINKABLE! I WOULDN'T HAVE DEAN IN THE TEAM AT ANY PRICE. HE'S VULGAR AND ILL-MANNERED!
DON'T WORRY. I'LL RAISE A TEAM OF MY OWN. MAYBE EVEN GO IN FOR THE COMPETITION AND TAKE THE CUP AWAY FROM YOU.
YOU DON'T UNDERSTAND. THE CHALLENGE CUP ISN'T OPEN TO JUST ANYBODY. IT'S FOR COUNTY CLUBS—AND WE'RE THE OFFICIAL SOUTHSHIRE SIDE!
AT THAT MOMENT, DIGGER'S ATTENTION WAS DIVERTED...
STONE THE CROWS! WHAT'S MY ABO PAL UP TO?
HE'S GONE TO LOOK FOR THE BALL YOU HIT... TO KEEP AS A SOUVENIR.
INSIDE THE TOP OF THE TOWER...
HERE'S THE BALL, BOSS. IT FELL AMONG ALL THESE OLD PAPERS.
THESE ARE FAMILY PAPERS, HUNDREDS OF YEARS OLD! JIM-JIM... I THINK I'VE GOT SURPRISING NEWS FOR COUSIN CLARENCE.
LISTEN, SPORT. THESE OLD FAMILY DEEDS SHOW THAT THE DEAN ESTATE WAS NEVER PART OF SOUTHSHIRE. IT WAS CREATED A SEPARATE SHIRE SIX HUNDRED YEARS AGO. I CAN RAISE MY OWN DEANSHIRE COUNTY CRICKET TEAM!
AND HERE'S MY TEAM! WE'RE GOING TO ENTER FOR THE CHALLENGE CUP AND WE MEAN TO WIN IT— SO YOU'D BETTER LOOK OUT!

NEXT MORNING . . .
YOUR MORNING TEA, SIR . . . AND WOULD YOU LIKE ME TO RUN YOUR BATH?

MISTER CLARENCE! CAN YOU COME AT ONCE?

THE BED HASN'T BEEN SLEPT IN, SIR. IT IS JUST AS I TURNED IT DOWN LAST NIGHT. IT APPEARS THAT THE — ER — PERSON FROM AUSTRALIA AND HIS FRIEND DECIDED TO LEAVE US.
THANK GOODNESS FOR THAT, PERKINS. HE MUST HAVE REALISED THAT HE WOULD NEVER FIT IN HERE AND DECIDED TO GO BACK TO HIS SMELLY SHEEP-STATION!

PERKINS, LOOK AT THAT SMOKE! IT CAN'T BE A GARDENER BURNING RUBBISH AT THIS TIME IN THE MORNING! SOUND THE ALARM!

AT THE SOUND OF THE FIRE BELL THE STAFF OF DEAN TOWERS RUSHED INTO ACTION, BUT . . .
TOP O' THE MORNING, CLARRY. YOU'RE JUST IN TIME FOR BREAKFAST.

UGH! TAKE THOSE THINGS AWAY!
NOT HUNGRY, BOSS? YOU SHOULD TRY SLEEPING IN A TENT.
CLARRY, GET ALL THE FAMILY TOGETHER. I'D LIKE TO TALK TO THEM . . .

LATER...
WHAT DOES HE WANT TO SAY TO US? IS HE GOING TO TURN US OUT?
I DON'T KNOW, UNCLE THEODORE. BUT HE'S THE HEAD OF THE FAMILY NOW. HE'D BE WITHIN HIS RIGHTS, THE COARSE BOUNDER.

GREAT-AUNT AGATHA, UNCLE THEODORE, COUSIN RODNEY, CLARRY, I UNDERSTAND THIS HAS ALWAYS BEEN YOUR FAMILY HOME. FEEL FREE TO GO ON USING THE JOINT. I PREFER A TENT!
THIS IS MOST GENEROUS OF YOU, CEDRIC MY BOY.

BUT COP THIS, ALL OF YOU. DON'T EVER CALL ME CEDRIC UNLESS YOU WANT ME TO DO MY BLOCK. I'M DIGGER TO MY MATES!

AND THAT WAS JUST YOUR JOKE, CED-ER-DIGGER, ABOUT FORMING A DEAMSHIRE CRICKET TEAM? IT'S IMPOSSIBLE. THERE ARE ONLY A FEW HUNDRED PEOPLE IN THE VILLAGE.
I NEVER JOKE ABOUT CRICKET, CLARRY. WHY SHOULDN'T I RAISE A TEAM? THERE'S ME AND JIM-JIM, FOR A START! . . .

AS DIGGER TURNED TO LEAVE
PING!
THE MING BOWL! A FAMILY HEIRLOOM! IT'S PRICELESS!

PERKINS, THE BUTLER, ENTERED AT THAT MOMENT. HE AMAZED DIGGER WITH THE SPEED AT WHICH HE MOVED . . .
STONE THE FLAMIN' CROWS! THAT WAS A SMART PIECE OF FIELDING, SPORT!

BRING HIM OUTSIDE, JIM-JIM. WE'VE GOT TO PUT HIM THROUGH HIS PACES.
WHAT DO YOU WANT WITH ME, SIR? WH-WHAT ARE YOU GOING TO DO WITH THOSE SWORDS?
?

PRAY USE YOUR INFLUENCE TO MAKE YOUR FRIEND DESIST. I HAVE URGENT TASKS AWAITING ME IN THE PANTRY.

?
SO CLARRY THINKS I CAN'T RAISE A TEAM, EH? IF YOU'RE AS GOOD A WICKET-KEEPER AS I THINK, I ONLY NEED TO FIND EIGHT MORE PLAYERS...

!
OUR BUTLER AS A WICKET-KEEPER! IF THIS IS A FAIR SAMPLE OF CEDRIC'S PLAN FOR RAISING A TEAM, HE'LL MAKE US THE LAUGHING STOCK OF THE CRICKET WORLD.
I'VE GOT TO STOP HIM, UNCLE THEO, AND YOU'LL HAVE TO HELP ME!

YOU'RE CHUCKING UP SOME ROUGH ONES, JIM-JIM. BUT NEVER MIND. IT'S GIVING PERKY THE CHANCE TO SHOW WHAT HE CAN DO.
CLUNK!
SNICK!

FAIR DINKUM, SPORT! THERE AREN'T MANY WICKET-KEEPERS WHO CAN MOVE FAST ENOUGH TO CATCH ME OUT OF MY GROUND.
ZAT!
ZONK!

HEY, YOU LAYABOUTS! COME AND GIVE PERKY AND JIM-JIM SOME HELP WITH THE FIELDING. THE EXERCISE WILL DO YOU GOOD.

UNCLE THEODORE AND COUSIN RODNEY OBEYED, BUT CLARENCE TURNED AWAY IN DISGUST.
TRAITORS!
BUT MY DEAR BOY, HE'S HEAD OF THE FAMILY NOW AND HE'S ALLOWING US TO GO ON LIVING HERE. WE MUST HUMOUR HIM.

DIGGER'S NEW RECRUITS WEREN'T MUCH HELP...
OW! WHO DID THAT?
THWACK!
YOU APPEAR TO HAVE SCORED A BOUNDARY ON BRACKETT, YOUR HEAD GARDENER, DEAR BOY.

IT LANDED RIGHT IN MY PETUNIAS. THEY'RE ALL BRUISED AND BATTERED!
SORRY, SPORT. IT SOUNDS PAINFUL. BUT HOW DID I KNOW YOU WERE HIDING BEHIND THERE?

HERE. TAKE YOUR BALL AND LET ME GET ON WITH MY WORK!

STONE THE CROWS! WHAT A THROW! DID YOU TRY TO DO THAT?
ZOOM

HAVE ANOTHER SHOT. SEE WHAT YOU CAN DO AT THAT END, SPORT.
?

YOU MEAN LIKE THIS?
!
CLANG!

MY PETUNIAS—!
NEVER MIND THE PETUNIAS, SPORT. WE'VE GOT TO GET YOU INTO TRAINING FOR THE TEAM. YOU'VE GOT AN EYE LIKE A FLAMIN' HAWK!
WE NEED PRACTICE NETS, BOSS. THIS JUST THE JOB.
BUT THAT NETTING IS TO KEEP THE BIRDS FROM EATING MY STRAWBERRIES.
THEN THE BIRDS ARE IN FOR A RIGHT NOSH-UP, AREN'T THEY, SPORT?
DEAR BOY, YOU'RE NOT REALLY SERIOUS ABOUT RAISING A DEANSHIRE TEAM FROM LOCAL YOKELS?
ZUNK!
TOO RIGHT I AM, UNCLE THEO. WE'RE ALREADY PROPERLY REGISTERED AS A COUNTY CLUB, AND I'M POSTING OFF OUR ENTRY FOR THE KNOCK-OUT CHALLENGE CUP TODAY.
UNCLE THEODORE WHEEZED AWAY TO REPORT WHAT HE HAD LEARNT TO CLARENCE.
ENTRIES FOR THE KNOCK-OUT CUP CLOSE TOMORROW. WE MUST MAKE SURE THE LETTER ARRIVES TOO LATE. THE POSTBOX WON'T HAVE BEEN CLEARED YET. UNCLE THEO—YOU'VE GOT TO HELP...
AH, SCROGGS. A MOST UNFORTUNATE THING HAS HAPPENED. I DROPPED A LETTER IN THERE BY MISTAKE. I WONDER IF I MIGHT HAVE IT BACK?
YOU SHOULD KNOW BETTER THAN TO ASK ME THAT, MISTER THEODORE. TAMPERING WITH THE QUEEN'S MAILS, AND ALL THAT. ONCE SOMETHING IS DROPPED IN THIS HERE BOX—
THEN UNCLE THEO JOGGED THE OLD POSTMAN SO THAT HIS SPECS FELL OFF...
YOU CLUMSY MAN, YOU.
SORRY, SCROGGS.
GOT IT!

OF COURSE WE'RE NOT ACTUALLY *STEALING* THE LETTER. JUST, FOR THE SAKE OF THE FAMILY'S GOOD NAME, DELAYING IT A LITTLE. WE'LL RE-POST IT TOMORROW.
BUT THERE IS NO HARM IN STEAMING IT OPEN TO MAKE SURE WE GOT THE RIGHT ONE.

THE HOT STEAM CAUSED THE ENVELOPE TO FLY OPEN.
DIGGER! Y-YOU GUESSED WE'D TRY AND STEAL THE ENVELOPE!
EVER BEEN HAD, SPORTS?
SURE THING, UNCLE THEO. AND OUR POSTMAN ISN'T AS DAFT AS YOU THINK. BESIDES, HIS BOY IS ONE OF MY FAST BOWLERS!

I'VE FIXED UP A TRIAL MATCH FOR MY LADS, BEFORE WE GO INTO THIS COMPETITION. THE TRAVELLERS ARE COMING DOWN TO GIVE US A KNOCK.
THE TRAVELLERS? YOU'RE JOKING! THEY'RE ONE OF THE BEST CLUB SIDES IN THE COUNTY.

DIGGER COULDN'T BEAR TO LIVE IN THE BIG HOUSE. HE AND HIS ABORIGINAL PAL JIM-JIM WERE CAMPING IN THE GROUNDS.
HI, SPORTS, YOU'RE JUST IN TIME FOR COFFEE.
DON'T BE IMPUDENT. WE'RE LOOKING FOR CEDRIC DEAN.
AND I'M SURE HE DOESN'T WANT TRAMPS LIGHTING FIRES ON HIS PLACE. YOU'D BETTER BE OFF!

DIGGER INTRODUCED HIMSELF...
IT'S AS WE SUSPECTED! THIS APPLICATION FROM A DEANSHIRE TEAM TO ENTER OUR COMPETITION IS JUST A HOAX.
WE'RE FROM THE COMPETITION MANAGEMENT COMMITTEE... WE WERE SENT TO VET THE CLUB AND DECIDE WHETHER IT WAS GOOD ENOUGH TO QUALIFY.

I NEVER JOKE ABOUT CRICKET, SPORTS. THE TRAVELLERS ARE PLAYING MY TEAM TOMORROW. YOU'D BETTER STAY AND WATCH.
THE TRAVELLERS! IF YOU'RE GOOD ENOUGH TO BEAT THEM, WE'LL ACCEPT YOU. THAT'S A PROMISE.

WHEN THE TRAVELLERS C.C. PLAYERS ARRIVED AT DEAN TOWERS NEXT DAY—
GOOD OF YOU TO INVITE US DOWN, CLARENCE. ALWAYS ENJOY PLAYING ON YOUR PARK.
DON'T THANK ME. I'M NOT EVEN PLAYING. YOU'RE DIGGER'S GUESTS.

WHEN THE VISITORS SAW THEIR OPPONENTS, THEY WERE EVEN MORE SHOCKED...
DEAN, IS THIS SOME KIND OF JOKE? IF YOU REALLY INVITED US HERE TO PLAY THIS ABSURD BUNCH OF MISFITS...
PULL YER NECK IN, SPORT. MY COBBERS MAY BE A BIT SHORT ON THE PROPER GEAR, BUT WE'LL GIVE YOU A GOOD GAME.

THE VISITING SKIPPER WON THE TOSS AND DECIDED TO BAT FIRST.
I SUPPOSE WE OUGHT TO KEEP OUR PROMISE AND SEE THEM PLAY—THOUGH IT'LL BE A COMPLETE WASTE OF TIME.

BOSS, WE'RE ONE PLAYER SHORT.
I FORGOT TO TELL YOU. ALFIE EVANS WON'T BE COMING. HE'S GONE ON THE BELLRINGERS' OUTING.
!
STONE THE CROWS! NOW HE TELLS ME! I'VE GOT TO FIND A SPARE MAN—AND FAST!

DIGGER RUSHED TO THE KITCHEN!
BUT, SIR—I HAVE TO PREPARE DINNER FOR THE FAMILY—
THIS IS MORE IMPORTANT. I'M A MAN SHORT. YOU'LL HAVE TO MAKE THE NUMBER UP.
!

THE VISITORS PLAYED THEMSELVES IN AGAINST THE BOWLING OF DIGGER AND JIM-JIM, THEN BEGAN TO LASH OUT...
CRACK!
CATCH IT—ONE OF YOU!

KRUNCH!
OOF!
THEY BOTH MISSED IT!
THEY'VE GIVEN AWAY FOUR RUNS!

DIGGER'S RAG-TAG TEAM HAD EVERYTHING TO LEARN ABOUT FIELDING.
SUFFERING KANGAROOS! YOU'RE NOT PLAYING FOOTBALL! GET YOUR HANDS BEHIND THE BALL!
!

AAAH!
LOOK OUT, YOU CLUMSY OAF.
?
!
TRIP!

I'M SURE WE CAN STOP WORRYING, UNCLE THEO. A FEW MORE MINUTES OF THIS NONSENSE WILL FINISH OFF THE DEANSHIRE CRICKET TEAM. THIS IS THEIR FIRST MATCH—AND THEIR LAST!

DIGGER WAS DISMAYED TO SEE THAT THE TWO IMPORTANT SPECTATORS WERE PREPARING TO LEAVE . . .
YOU CAN'T GO YET. YOU PROMISED TO LET US ENTER THE KNOCK-OUT CUP IF WE WON THIS GAME !
THERE'S NO POINT IN WASTING ANY MORE TIME. WE'VE SEEN ENOUGH.

I INTEND TO MAKE CRICKETERS OUT OF THIS BUNCH OF HAM-FISTED DRONGOES IF IT KILLS ME! BEFORE THIS MATCH IS OVER, I'LL PROVE IT !
VERY WELL – IF YOU.. ER.. INSIST – WE'LL WATCH A FEW MORE OVERS !

WHEN PLAY WAS RESUMED . . .
DIGGER'S TAKING HIMSELF OFF! HE'S GIVING THE BOWLING TO LENNY SCROGGS, THE POSTMAN'S BOY.
WHAT'S DIGGER THINKING OF ? LENNY HAS ONLY JUST LEFT SCHOOL !

CONTEMPTUOUSLY, THE BATSMAN LASHED LENNY'S FIRST DELIVERY FOR SIX.
THAT'S THE THIRTY UP – AND THEY COULD GO ON HITTING THAT STUFF ALL DAY.
THWAK!

LENNY'S NEXT ONE LOOKED EQUALLY SIMPLE . . .
HE MISSED IT ! THAT SHOULD HAVE BEEN ANOTHER SIX !

HUH ?
HOW WAS IT ?
OUT!
CLACK!
THE NEXT MAN IN FOUND LENNY'S FIRST BALL EASY TO HIT . . .
COME ON, PLENTY OF TIME FOR ANOTHER RUN !
BRACKETT, THE GARDENER, WAS LUMBERING TOWARDS THE BALL . . .

THE BOWLING IS TRIPE, BUT WATCH OUT FOR THAT WICKET-KEEPER. HE'S PERKINS, THE FAMILY BUTLER. HE MOVES A LOT FASTER THAN YOU'D IMAGINE.

CONTINUED ON PAGE 97.

"I DON'T CARE IF THEY DO HELP YOUR SLIDING TACKLE – TAKE THEM OFF !"
"WASN'T IT CLEVER THE WAY OUR GOALKEEPER KEPT AVOIDING THAT MUDDY BALL ?"
CITY

FOOTBALL

"IT LOOKS LIKE UNITED ARE ON THE DEFENSIVE TODAY !"
"IS THERE ANY DOUBT ABOUT MY FUTURE WITH THIS CLUB, BOSS ?"

"HE'S THEIR FULL-BACK !"
"HE SHOULD BE ON MASTERMIND – HE NEVER PASSES !"

FUNNIES

GET-WELL-SOON
CARDS
"GIVE ME ELEVEN, PLEASE !"
"WE CAN'T CHOP IT DOWN–IT'S A PROTECTED TREE !"
3
7

"WE'VE GOT A GOOD YOUTH POLICY HERE—WE SIGNED HIM FOR A FEW BUBBLE GUMS, SOME MARBLES AND A CONKER !"
7
COACH
"BUT, REF, IT WAS A FAIR TACKLE !"
"AT THIS GROUND THE CROWDS ARE SO SMALL THAT THEY ANNOUNCE THE CROWD CHANGES FIRST !"
"OWN UP THE ROTTER WHO TIED THAT LOOSE END OF MY JERSEY TO THE BALL BEFORE I TOOK THE GOAL-KICK !"

THE SUPER SIXTEEN!

A SPECIAL SELECTION OF SENSATIONAL SPORTS STARS!

The first sports personality to feature in this series, brilliant young golfer from Spain, Severiano Ballesteros, has had a meteoric rise to fame—17 tournament wins in 4 years, before his greatest triumph of winning the British Open trophy, above, in 1979, at the

TOUGH THOMPSON!

Although Daley Thompson is pictured throwing the discus, he has to compete in TEN sports for his 'toughest of all' event—the Decathlon. Commonwealth Games gold medal winner, Daley can claim to be Britain's best 'all-rounder.

His bowling action isn't the tidiest example, but when Bob gets in the groove, he is a truly formidable opening bowler for Warwickshire and England, achieving lift on even placid pitches. He was greatly missed by England in the 1979 Prudential World Cup Final, due to injury.

WHIRLWIND WILLIS!

Another cricketer who has become an England regular like Bob Willis, is Graham Gooch of Essex. Before the 1979 season, Essex had never won a major trophy, until Graham's century in the Benson & Hedges Cup Final virtually won that trophy he's holding!

GRAHAM IS GREAT!

WHAT A HORSE!

he greatest British-ed horse since igadier Gerard, Troy dden by Willie Carson d a fantastic season 1979, winning the Epsom Derby, the Irish Sweeps Derby and the Benson & Hedges Cup. After that, the champion horse was syndicated for 7.2 MILLION pounds!

MOTOCROSS MARVEL!

Moto-cross is a sport not often in the headlines, so did you know that the British rider pictured here, won the World 500cc Championship in 1979? He's Graham Noyce, who also won the British Championship on his Honda bike—and not for the first time, either!

GEOFF THE GIANT!

Britain's most consistent shot-putter and British Champion for many years, Geoff Capes has won a host of international honours and even appeared in the Guinness Book of Records, by lifting 51 car tyres weighing 347 kilograms (765 lb) on the BBC Record Breakers TV programme!

MIGHTY McENROE!

When American John McEnroe first burst on the tennis scene, he was nick-named 'Superbrat' because of his temperamental out-bursts on court. But now he's settled down as a player of great class and is changing that nickname to 'SuperSTAR'!

RISING STARS

Following in his father Harvey's footsteps, that's Robert Smith as he negotiates the steep bank at Hickstead on the way to winning the Grand Prix there in 1979. Two other top prizes he won that year riding his horse, Video, were the King George V Gold Cup and the Leading Show Jumper of the Year. A star of the present and the future!

BARRY IS BEST!

During his hazardous career, Barry Sheene has broken most of the bones in his body! But that didn't stop him winning the 500cc World Championship in 1976 and 1977 and finishing second last year. This superb photo was taken during the 1979 British Grand Prix, where he finished second to World Champion, Kenny Roberts.

MARTIN'S MARVELLOUS MINI

MARTIN BAKER OWNED A RACING MINI WHICH HE CALLED "GEORGE". WITH HIS PAL, TINY HILL, MARTIN WENT TO A REMOTE PART OF SCOTLAND, TO TAKE PART IN SOMETHING CALLED... A *"NO ROAD RACE"*!

WE'VE NEVER ENTERED A RACE LIKE THIS BEFORE. WHAT ***IS*** A *NO ROAD RACE?*

YOU JUST HAVE TO KEEP OFF THE ROADS, THAT'S ALL! IT'S A CROSS-COUNTRY EVENT. YOUR BEST ROUTE IS TO KEEP EAST OF THE RIVER...

NO ROAD RACE START

TIGER

I TOLD YOU IT WAS TOO TOUGH FOR THAT CAR, CHUM!
PUSH HARDER! HAW, HAW!
DON'T LISTEN TO THEM, TINY!

EVENTUALLY THEY GOT GOING AGAIN!
I CAN'T SEE ANY OF THEM! WE'RE MILES BEHIND ALREADY!
YES! ALL BECAUSE OF THAT ROTTEN HEDGE!

TINY CONSULTED HIS MAP...
IF WE GO EAST OF THE RIVER, AS THAT MAN SAID... WE HAVE TO GO IN A WIDE CURVE. IF WE CROSS THE RIVER... WE CAN GO IN A STRAIGHT LINE AND CUT OFF MILES!
LET'S TRY IT, THEN!

MARTIN CHANGED COURSE...
THERE'S BOUND TO BE A BRIDGE OF SOME SORT OVER THE RIVER...
WATCH WHERE YOU'RE GOING! MIND THE TREES!

I KNOW I SAID WE COULD GO IN A STRAIGHT LINE... BUT THIS IS RIDICULOUS!
I KNEW THEY WERE THERE!

THERE'S THE RIVER, BY THE FARMHOUSE...
I BET THERE'S A BRIDGE THERE! THE FARMER WOULD WANT TO GET ACROSS, WOULDN'T HE?

THE FARMER MET THEM...
THERE'S NO BRIDGE, MISTER! I ONLY GO OVER THE WATER TO FETCH STRAY ANIMALS...AND THEN I GO BY BOAT...

IT ISN'T MUCH OF A BOAT. I PULL IT ACROSS BY THE ROPES...
WE WON'T GET GEORGE ACROSS ON IT...
WE COULD TRY...

THE WATER'S COMING OVER THE SIDE ALREADY!
WE'D BETTER GET A SHIFT ON THEN!

THE WATER'S COMING IN FAST!
IT'S YOUR WEIGHT!

THEY TRIED TO MOVE FASTER BY PULLING HARDER...
STONE ME! IT'S COMING IN EVEN WORSE NOW!
WE'VE HAD IT!
SECONDS LATER...
HEY, IT'S NOT ALL THAT DEEP!
WE MIGHT BE ABLE TO DRIVE GEORGE ON THE STARTER THE REST OF THE WAY!

THEY TRIED IT...
OOOERR... WE'RE GOING DEEPER!
GEORGE
TIGER
5
IT'S OKAY... WE'VE JUST COME OFF THE BOAT, THAT'S ALL!

KEEP GOING! WE'RE NEARLY OUT!
TIGER
GEORGE
LOOK AT IT THE OTHER WAY... AND WE'RE NEARLY BACK IN, AREN'T WE?

BUT...
WE'VE MADE IT!
WE MUST HAVE CUT OFF NEARLY TWENTY MILES! WE COULD EVEN BE AHEAD OF EVERYONE ELSE NOW!

HELLO, WHAT'S THIS?
WE'D BETTER STOP... IT LOOKS LIKE A FENCE AROUND A QUARRY OR SOMETHING!

A RAILWAY LINE! IT'S ON THE MAP. BUT IT'S DIS-USED NOW...
THAT'S PROBABLY ANOTHER REASON WHY IT'S BETTER TO KEEP EAST OF THE RIVER. HOW DO WE GET OVER THIS?

HEY, I'VE GOT AN IDEA! IS THERE A ROPE IN GEORGE?
YES, WE ALWAYS CARRY ONE FOR EMERGENCIES! BUT WHAT'S THE IDEA? I MEAN... YOU GET SOME DAFT ONES AT TIMES!

I DON'T GET IT! WE CAN LOWER GEORGE DOWN EASILY ENOUGH... BUT THE TWO OF US WILL NEVER PULL HIM UP THE FAR SIDE!
WE DON'T HAVE TO...
5

THE RAILWAY LINE CURVES FURTHER ON... AND GOES THE WAY WE WANT TO GO...
YOU CAN'T DRIVE GEORGE ALONG A RAILWAY TRACK, MARTIN!
GEORGE

NO, BUT WE CAN DRIVE **ON** THE LINES... THEY'RE JUST THE RIGHT SIZE FOR GEORGE!
THAT'S **GREAT**... AND I THOUGHT **I** WAS THE ONE WITH ALL THE BRAINS!
TIGER
GEORGE
TIGER
5

WE DON'T EVEN HAVE TO STEER!
NO NEED TO READ THE MAP... WE **CAN'T** TURN IN THE WRONG DIRECTION!
TIGER
GEORGE
TIGER
5

THEY CAME TO A TUNNEL...
I HOPE THEY HAVEN'T FILLED THE TUNNEL IN HALFWAY THROUGH!
DON'T BE DAFT! WHAT WOULD ANYONE DO THAT FOR?

HERE, I DON'T FANCY THIS. IT'S CREEPY!
YES. I'LL BE GLAD WHEN WE'RE OUT...

FIVE MINUTES LATER...
MADE IT! GOSH, AM I GLAD TO BE BACK IN DAYLIGHT!
WELL, LET'S GET THE TYRES BACK ON... WE CAN DRIVE ACROSS-COUNTRY AGAIN NOW...

IT TOOK THEM TWENTY MINUTES TO REPLACE AND INFLATE THE TYRES...
HOW MUCH FURTHER, OLD PAL?
ACCORDING TO MY MAP... WE'RE NEARLY THERE!
GEORGE
TIGER
5

AT THE FINISH LINE...
ROAD RACE FINISH
THERE'S SOMETHING COMING!
CAN YOU SEE A CAR, JOHN?
I'M JUST GETTING IT IN FOCUS...

I DON'T BELIEVE IT! IT'S THE MINI... MARTIN AND TINY!
GEORGE
TIGER
5

THE WINNERS! FIRST HOME... MARTIN BAKER AND TINY HILL!
NO ROAD RA
FINISH
HURRRAHHH!
I DON'T KNOW HOW THEY DID IT IN THAT LITTLE CAR!
THEY'RE FANTASTIC DRIVERS!
TIGER
GEORGE
15

LATER, AFTER THE OTHER CARS HAD FINISHED...
HOW DID YOU MANAGE TO FINISH AHEAD OF US, CHUM? WHAT'S YOUR SECRET?
YES... TELL US...
I DIDN'T THINK YOU'D EVEN GET THROUGH THAT FIRST HEDGE!

I THINK YOU COULD SAY... WE BOTH PULLED OUR WEIGHT!
AND — AND DROVE ON THE RIGHT LINES! THAT'S ALL THERE WAS TO IT! APART FROM HAVING THE BEST CAR!

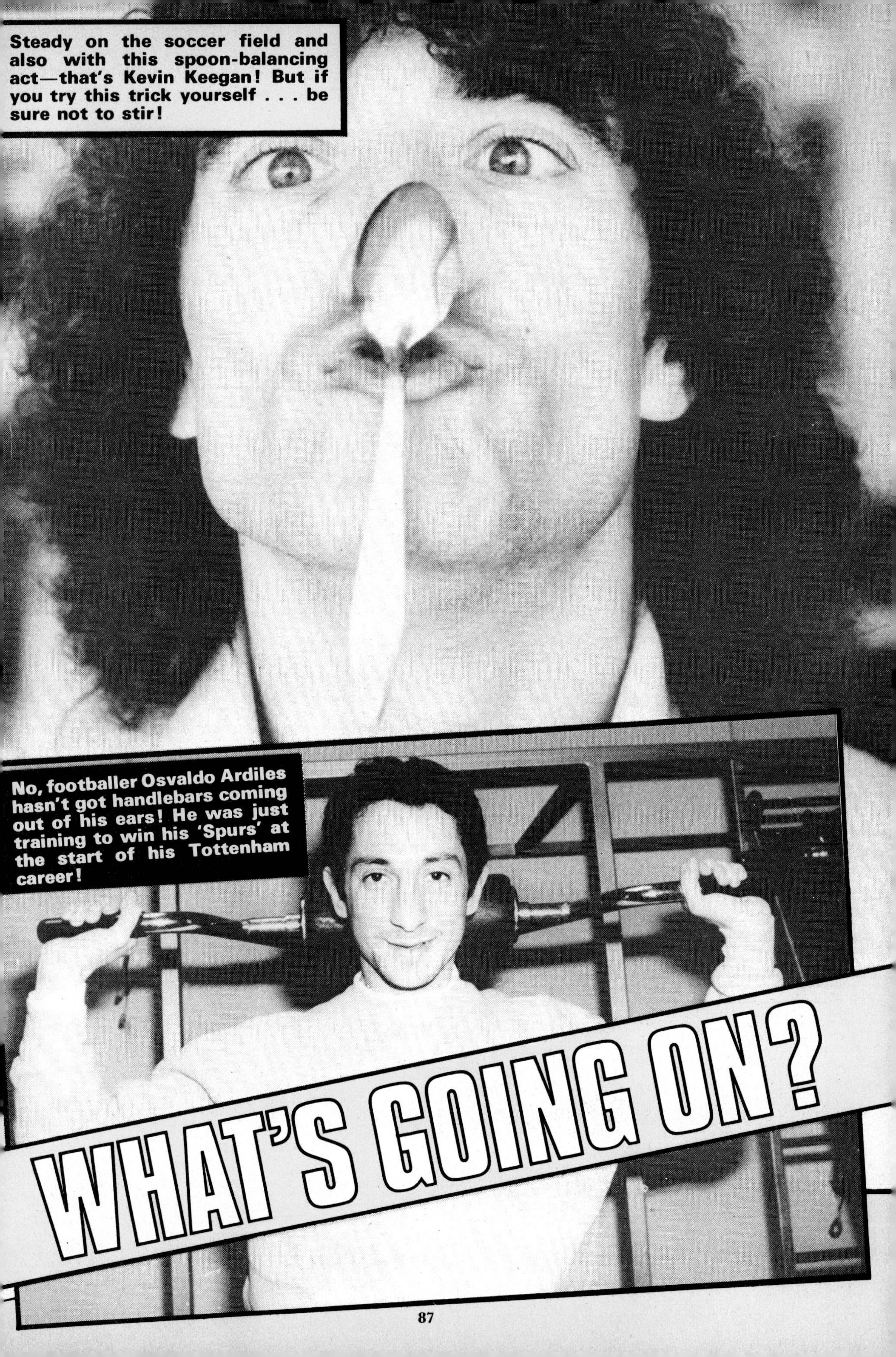

Steady on the soccer field and also with this spoon-balancing act—that's Kevin Keegan! But if you try this trick yourself . . . be sure not to stir!

No, footballer Osvaldo Ardiles hasn't got handlebars coming out of his ears! He was just training to win his 'Spurs' at the start of his Tottenham career!

Flexing their muscles at Crystal Palace National Sports Centre were the members of a newly-formed, all-girl, five-a-side, soccer Show-biz team. Even if they don't score any goals, we bet every match they play is a real sell-out!

The two stars at the top of the next page aren't boxers! But Peter Shilton and Ray Clemence are always having 'fights'—to see who can produce the best form, to win the honour of being England's goalkeeper!

The driver right, wouldn't win a Formula One Grand Prix in his strange car! But he did win the Shell mileage marathon, by covering 1,684 miles—on one gallon of petrol!

KING'S · COLLEGE
MECHANICAL ENGINEERING
LONDON

When England cricket captain Mike Brearley was asked to unlock the doors of a famous London store for their summer sale, he took no chances and wore his protective crash helmet! Then he joined the bargain-hunters in the china department . . . and made a 'catch' he daren't drop!

A great stroke from the world's number one tennis star, Bjorn Borg! But if you study the photo carefully, it appears that Bjorn is also juggling with two strange objects just above his left hand! However, it's only an optical illusion and the 'objects' are special microphones at the back of the court to pick up the sound of the ball being hit!

A competition to find the strongest man in Holland provided plenty of headaches for the competitors, as you can see, right! Gerard du Prie also had to tear up telephone directories and pull heavy trunks. But for the iron-bar bending event—he found it really paid to use his head!

West Ham and England soccer star Trevor Brooking has never let success go to his head—but he couldn't stop a pancake landing on it (above), while giving some tips to a bevy of beauty queens, training for an annual pancake race! Ah, well, Trevor, if you don't succeed at first—fry, fry, fry again!

This person seems remarkably happy for someone who looks like he's about to hit himself on the head (left)! Actually, Luther Blissett had just scored two goals for Watford, to put them in the next round of the League Cup and he was demonstrating how he was going to 'hammer' their next opponents!

KING OF THE TRACK

BILL BOSTON WAS FIRST TO OFFER HIS CONGRATULATIONS!

WELL DONE, PAL! . . . THAT WAS CLOSE! I HOPE YOU'LL GIVE ME A CHANCE TO GET MY REVENGE ON SATURDAY . . . I'VE GOT A CROWD OF RIDERS TO TAKE PART IN COLONEL GRANT'S CROSS-COUNTRY SCRAMBLE RACE, FOR CHARITY— WILL YOU TAKE PART?

GREAT! I'D LOVE TO! I CAN RIDE THE BIKE I USE FOR JUMPING!

THE GROUND'S PRETTY MUDDY ... SO IT'S GOING TO PAY TO HAVE AS FEW RIDERS AS POSSIBLE IN FRONT OF ME... I'LL TRY TO MOVE UP ANOTHER COUPLE OF PLACES RIGHT AWAY...
BUT THEN, AS BARRY TRIED HIS PLANNED MANOUEVRE...
BACK WHEEL'S SLIDING AWAY, I'VE LOST IT... AAARGH!
IT WASN'T MY BAD RIDING, EITHER... A PIECE OF ROPE'S GOT WRAPPED ROUND THE BACK WHEEL! OF ALL THE ROTTEN THINGS TO HAPPEN...
TOUGH LUCK, BARRY! SORRY I CAN'T STOP, OR I'LL GET BOGGED DOWN, TOO!
VALUABLE MINUTES WERE WASTED...
I'VE FREED IT... BUT MY MAP'S SOAKED AND USELESS...
... AND EVERYONE'S GONE! WHICH WAY DO I GO?
THEN...
HEY, THERE'S ANOTHER RIDER ... PERHAPS HE HAD A FALL, TOO! I'LL FOLLOW HIM...
HE SEEMS TO KNOW WHERE HE'S GOING, ANYWAY...

SOMETHING TELLS ME HE'S DONE THIS BEFORE!

HE MUST BE GOOD, BECAUSE EVERY TIME I SPEED UP, HE DOES THE SAME...
...STILL KEEPING THE SAME DISTANCE IN FRONT OF ME— AND HE HASN'T LOOKED BEHIND HIM ONCE!

NOW WHERE'S HE GOING? THAT MUST BE A HUGE DRAIN-PIPE FOR THE HILLSIDE...

OH, WELL, IF HE CAN DO IT... SO CAN I!

I WONDER WHAT'S AT THE OTHER END? THERE'S DAYLIGHT AHEAD...

BARRY SOON FOUND OUT!
THE RAILWAY RAVINE! I CAN'T STOP... SO MY ONLY CHANCE IS TO ACCELERATE!

IT'S A GOOD THING I'VE HAD EXPERIENCE AT JUMPING... BUT THIS WILL BE THE BIGGEST YET, IF I MAKE IT!

BIKE AND RIDER SEEMED TO HANG IN THE AIR!
OOOOEER! I DAREN'T LOOK DOWN!

I DON'T BELIEVE IT— I MADE IT!... PHEW! I WOULDN'T WANT TO DO THAT AGAIN! NO SIGN OF THAT RIDER I'VE BEEN FOLLOWING... HE MUST BE WELL AHEAD...
13

AT THE END OF THE RACE...
FINISH
AND FIRST OVER THE LINE IS... BARRY KING!
HURRAH! HE'S THE WINNER!
WHAT THE –?
13

BUT WHAT HAPPENED TO THE RIDER IN FRONT OF ME... THE ONE IN THE WHITE LEATHERS AND CHEQUERED HELMET?
NO-ONE WAS AHEAD OF YOU, SON... YOU'VE WON! NOW HURRY UP AND DISMOUNT... THE COLONEL'S WAITING TO PRESENT YOU WITH THE TROPHY!

BARRY RECEIVED A MAGNIFICENT CUP!
HURRAH! WELL DONE!
EXCUSE ME, YOUNG FELLER...
13
...BUT I COULDN'T HELP OVERHEARING ABOUT THE RIDER YOU SAW... IT SOUNDED LIKE THE GEAR THE COLONEL'S SON USED TO WEAR... BUT HE WAS KILLED YEARS AGO...
HOW?

HE TRIED TO JUMP THE RAILWAY RAVINE ON A MOTORBIKE... BUT IT'S IMPOSSIBLE...
...NO-ONE COULD EVER DO THAT AND LIVE!

The SLOGGER from DOWN UNDER

CONTINUED FROM PAGE 61

HE PLAYED EXACTLY THE SAME SWIPING STROKE TO THE NEXT DELIVERY. BUT THIS TIME HE HIT THE BALL!
SMACK!
A SIX!
BEN'S GOT HIS EYE IN NOW!
THE THIRD BALL WAS AS STRAIGHT AS AN ARROW . . .
GOOD DELIVERY!
BOWLED—ALL OVER THE PLACE!
PERKINS THE BUTLER CAME IN, WITH ORDERS TO STONEWALL AND LET DIGGER DO THE SCORING. BUT THE VERY FIRST BALL BROUGHT DISASTER . . .
?
HE'S TRODDEN ON HIS WICKET!
BRACKETT, THE HEAD GARDENER, HIT HIS FIRST BALL STRAIGHT UP INTO THE AIR . . .
BIAM!
IT'S GONE INTO ORBIT!
HE WAS EASILY CAUGHT. WITH ONLY 54 ON THE BOARD, DIGGER SETTLED DOWN TO A GRIM FIGHT, TRYING TO KEEP THE BOWLING TO HIMSELF . . .
EVERYONE CLOSE IN TO SAVE THE SINGLE.
HOW MANY BALLS TO COME?
ONE MORE.
THE RIVAL SKIPPER COUNTERED WITH TIGHT, CLOSED-IN FIELDING, BUT TIME AND AGAIN DIGGER FOUND A WAY THROUGH . . .
THEY'VE RUN ONE.
THERE'S TIME FOR ANOTHER!
STAY WHERE YOU ARE! ONE'S ALL WE NEED!
DEANSHIRE'S NINTH WICKET WENT AT 108. LENNY SCROGGS, THE YOUNGEST MEMBER OF THE TEAM, WAS LAST MAN IN . . .
THERE'S ONLY ONE BALL TO GO IN THIS OVER. GIVE THE KID AN EASY ONE THAT HE CAN HIT—WE'LL LET HIM TAKE A SINGLE . . . THEN WE'LL HAVE A WHOLE OVER TO BOWL AT HIM!
LENNY, BRIMMING WITH FALSE CONFIDENCE, TOOK THE TEMPTING BAIT . . .
COME ON, DIGGER. I WANT TO BREAK MY DUCK!
NO! STAY AT THAT END!
BUT LENNY HAD ALREADY BEGUN TO RUN, THREATENING LAST-MINUTE DISASTER TO ALL DIGGER'S EFFORTS . . .

THEY RAN THE SINGLE. THEN LENNY FACED THE NEW OVER...
IT'S AS GOOD AS FINISHED, UNCLE THEO. THEY'VE PUT THEIR FASTEST BOWLER ON — AND THIS BOY, LENNY SCROGGS, WON'T LAST THE OVER.
DON'T COUNT ON IT, CLARENCE. IF THE BOY CAN SCRAPE A SINGLE...

NOT A CHANCE, UNCLE THEO. LOOK, HE DOESN'T EVEN KNOW HOW TO HOLD HIS BAT!

THE BALL WAS A GOOD LENGTH. LENNY SHAPED AWKWARDLY, AND YET . . .
HE'S HIT IT!
A FLUKE!
ZONK!

THEY'VE RUN TWO.
FIVE MORE NEEDED.
ANOTHER?
NO — TOO RISKY. STAY. BUT NEVER MIND THE RUNS. JUST TRY TO KEEP YOUR END UP. REMEMBER YOU'RE OUR LAST MAN.

THE NEXT ONE POPPED UP SHORT. LENNY GAVE WAY TO TEMPTATION, IGNORING DIGGER'S ORDERS . . .
HE'S COME RIGHT OUT OF HIS GROUND!
IF HE MISSES HE'LL BE STUMPED, FOR SURE.

BUT LENNY DIDN'T MISS . . .
A SIX! THAT'S ALL WE NEEDED!
MY BOY LENNY HAS MADE THE WINNING HIT!

CONGRATULATIONS. THAT SIX EARNED YOU A PLACE IN THE KNOCKOUT COMPETITION. AS NEWCOMERS, YOU WILL BE REQUIRED TO PLAY IN A QUALIFYING ROUND NEXT SATURDAY. YOU'LL BE SENT FULL DETAILS IN A DAY OR TWO.
GOOD ON YER, SPORT! I ALWAYS KNEW MY COBBERS COULD DO IT.

ON FRIDAY MORNING, THE MYSTERY DEEPENED . . .

IF YOUR COUSIN CLARENCE HASN'T EXPLAINED, SIR, IT IS NOT FOR ME, THE GARDENER, TO SPEAK. PERHAPS YOU'D BETTER GO DOWN TO THE RIVER...
THE RIVER? WHAT'S THAT GOT TO DO WITH IT? COME ON, JIM-JIM. LET'S GET TO THE BOTTOM OF THIS MYSTERY.

DIGGER AND HIS ABORIGINAL PAL JIM-JIM RECEIVED A SHOCK WHEN THEY REACHED THE RIVER . . .
WHAT'S GOING ON?
?
WE'RE PRACTISING FOR THE MATCH!
BOSS, THESE ENGLISH FELLERS HAVE DONE THEIR BLOCKS! WHOEVER HEARD OF PRACTISING FOR CRICKET IN THIS WAY?

CLARENCE STROLLED UP WITH UNCLE THEODORE . . .
WHO SAID ANYTHING ABOUT CRICKET? THIS IS THE ANNUAL TUB BATTLE BETWEEN US AND THE NEXT VILLAGE. IT DATES BACK CENTURIES TO WHEN WE USED TO POACH EACH OTHER'S SALMON. EACH SIDE DEFENDS A BRIDGE AND WHOEVER GETS THE BALL THROUGH FIRST IS THE WINNER.

IT SOUNDS A GREAT IDEA. DO YOU THINK THEY'D LET ME HAVE A GO?
OF COURSE. YOU, AS LORD OF THE MANOR, WILL BE EXPECTED TO LEAD OUR SIDE.

COME ON, JIM-JIM. LET'S HAVE A BASH!

HOW LONG HAVE I GOT TO GET THE HANG OF THIS? WHEN DOES THE BATTLE COME OFF?
SATURDAY MORNING, NINE O'CLOCK.

BUT OUR CRICKET MATCH IS ON SATURDAY! THE LADS WILL BE EXHAUSTED BEFORE THEY START! WE'LL HAVE TO POSTPONE THE TUB BATTLE!
CRASH!
SPLOSH!
YOU CAN'T DO THAT. IT'S ALWAYS BEEN HELD ON THE SAME SATURDAY, FOR HUNDREDS OF YEARS!

HE'S GIVING US THE BRUSH-OFF, JIM-JIM. IT'S GOING TO BE HARD TO FILL HIS PLACE, BUT I WASN'T GOING TO LET HIM KNOW THAT. WE'LL MANAGE SOMEHOW.

BUT WORSE WAS TO FOLLOW . . .

BEGGING YOUR PARDON, SIR, BUT I'LL NOT BE PLAYING TOMORROW. I'LL BE BUSY IN THE POTTING SHED.

THAT MEANS TWO PLACES TO FILL!

HEY, DIGGER. HERE'S PERKINS, YOUR BUTLER, AND BRACKETT YOUR HEAD GARDENER. LOOK AT THE FAB GEAR!
ARE THEY JOINING IN THIS, TOO?
OF COURSE. THE WHOLE VILLAGE TAKES PART.

ARE THESE SOME MORE OF OUR COBBERS? THEY LOOK LIKE A TROOP OF GORILLAS.
THOSE, SIR, ARE SOME OF OUR OPPONENTS. THEY'RE THE TEAM FROM THE NEXT VILLAGE.

THE CONTEST WAS OFFICIALLY STARTED BY THE LOCAL MAYOR...
PLAY! THE FIRST SIDE TO GET THE BALL UNDER ITS OPPONENTS' BRIDGE IS THE WINNER.

SO FAR AS DIGGER COULD JUDGE, THERE WERE NO RULES...
STONE THE CROWS, JIM-JIM! IF THIS LASTS LONG WE WON'T HAVE ANYBODY WHO'S FIT TO PLAY CRICKET.
OOF!
ZONK!

THE DEAN TOWERS GOAL SOON CAME UNDER HEAVY ATTACK...
WELL PLAYED, DIGGER!
POW!

LOOK AT THE TIME— A QUARTER PAST TEN. OUR CRICKET MATCH STARTS AT ELEVEN.
SOMETIMES THE GAME LASTS ALL DAY BEFORE SOMEONE SCORES!
!

THE MIDSHIRE TEAM HAD JUST ARRIVED AT THE CLUB HOUSE, TO BE GREETED BY COUSIN CLARENCE.
WHERE ARE DIGGER AND HIS TEAM?
YOU'LL FIND THEM ALL DOWN ON THE RIVER.

?
!
IS THAT DIGGER DEAN? WHAT'S GOING ON?

COME ON, SPORT! WE'VE GOT TO FINISH THIS OFF— AND FAST!

LOOK AT DIGGER, HE'S GONE BERSERK!
CRACK!

DIGGER'S SCORED! WE'VE WON!

NOW WE CAN GET ON WITH THE CRICKET MATCH. EVERYONE WHO'S IN THE TEAM—GET CHANGED!

BUT WHEN THE TEAM BEGAN TO ARRIVE...
STONE THE CROWS! I'VE GOT TO PLAY THIS MATCH WITH A TEAM OF FLAMIN' CROCKS!

IF MY LOT HAVE TO FIELD IN THAT STATE, WE'RE SUNK. THERE'S JUST ONE CHANCE. IF I WIN THE TOSS WE'LL BAT FIRST, AND GIVE THEM SOME TIME TO RECOVER!

YOUR CALL, COBBER!
HEADS.

HEADS, IT IS. WE'LL TAKE FIRST KNOCK.
OH, DEAR, THAT MEANS WE FIELD STRAIGHT AWAY!
THAT'S OUR LAST HOPE GONE!

JIM-JIM, THE RULES OF THE COMPETITION ALLOW THEM A MAXIMUM OF THREE HOURS BATTING. THEY'LL HAVE TO TAKE RISKS AND GO FOR RUNS.

BUT THE MIDSHIRE OPENER PLAYED DIGGER'S FIRST OVER FOR A CAUTIOUS MAIDEN. THEN, JIM-JIM, DIGGER'S ABORIGINAL PAL, CAME ON.
A WIDE... IT'S GONE FOR FOUR!
WHAT'S WRONG WITH JIM-JIM?

NOW WHAT'S JIM-JIM UP TO?
?

SUFFERING KANGAROOS! HE'S BOWLING LEFT-HANDED. THEY'LL KNOCK THAT STUFF ALL OVER THE FIELD.

DIGGER WAS RIGHT.
IT'S GOING FOR SIX!
CRACK!
THIS IS GOING TO BE A WALK-OVER!

JIM-JIM'S NEXT BALL LOOKED EQUALLY EASY...
!
HE'S OUT FOR SURE. JIM-JIM WAS BOWLING FOR A CATCH—AND HE NEVER MISSES!

STONE THE CROWS! HE'S DROPPED IT!
!

IT'S MY RIGHT SHOULDER, BOSS. IT'S FAIR CROOK. CAN'T SWING MY ARM.
I'LL HAVE TO PUT LENNY SCROGGS ON TO BOWL AT YOUR END. HE'S A BIT ERRATIC BUT THERE'S NO OTHER CHOICE!

MIDSHIRE SLOWED THEIR RATE OF SCORING AND WERE CAREFUL TO LOSE NO MORE WICKETS BEFORE LUNCH.

THEY'VE GOT ANOTHER HOUR'S BATTING. WE'LL NEVER GET 'EM ALL OUT. *IT'S JUST A MATTER OF TRYING TO KEEP THE RUNS DOWN SO THAT THEY DON'T SET US TOO MANY.*

70 RUNS WANTED, AND AN HOUR AND A HALF TO GET 'EM IN.
BUT ONLY TWO WICKETS TO FALL. IT ALL DEPENDS ON WHETHER DIGGER CAN KEEP THE BOWLING.

DIGGER HIT TWO BOUNDARIES OFF HIS OPENING OVER. FOR THE SIXTH BALL, THE MIDSHIRE SKIPPER MOVED HIS MEN IN CLOSE TO TRY TO STOP DIGGER SNEAKING A SINGLE, BUT . . .
COME ON!

THEY TRIED TO TEMPT PERKINS INTO RUNNING ANOTHER BY LETTING THE RETURNED BALL GO FOR AN OVERTHROW . . .
ANOTHER?
NO. STAY!

DIGGER'S POWERFUL AND ACCURATE HITTING WERE ENOUGH TO BREAK THE HEART OF ANY BOWLER . . .
ANOTHER SIX! DIGGER'S PUT THE HUNDRED UP!
CRACK!
48 WANTED. THERE'S PLENTY OF TIME BEFORE HALF PAST SIX, SO LONG AS DIGGER CAN KEEP THE BOWLING.

BUT WHEN, AT THE END OF THE OVER, HE AGAIN TRIED TO KEEP THE BOWLING BY SNEAKING A SINGLE . . .
CAN WE?
NO! TOO RISKY!

IF ONLY PERKINS CAN STAY THERE.
I THINK HE SHOULD GO FOR A SINGLE. IT'S LESS OF A RISK THAN TRYING TO SURVIVE SIX BALLS.

PERKINS PLAYED THE BALL WITH A DEAD BAT . . .
WELL DONE, SPORT!

BEFORE ANY FIELDER COULD TOUCH THE BALL, PERKINS HIT IT AGAIN . . .
COME ON, SIR! WE CAN TAKE ONE!
OH, NO! STONE THE FLAMIN' CROWS!
BLAM!

HOW WAS IT?
OUT!
I PROTEST! MY WICKET ISN'T BROKEN!

YOU'RE OUT, SPORT. YOU STRUCK AT THE BALL TWICE.
NO-ONE TOLD ME I WASN'T ALLOWED TO DO THAT. WHAT A SILLY RULE!

BRACKETT, THE GARDENER, WAS THE LAST MAN IN . . .
THERE'S FIVE BALLS TO COME. JUST CONCENTRATE ON KEEPING THEM OFF YOUR WICKET. NEVER MIND THE RUNS. LEAVE THOSE TO ME.

JUST AS BRACKETT WAS ABOUT TO RECEIVE HIS FIRST BALL . . .
WAIT! THE SUN'S IN MY EYES! SOMEONE BRING ME MY HAT!

BOWL FOR A CATCH. TRY TO MAKE HIM HIT IT INTO THE AIR.

BRACKETT COULDN'T RESIST THE TEMPTATION TO TAKE A SWIPE AT THE MEDIUM-PACED BALL WHICH ROSE UP, JUST ASKING TO BE HIT . . .
HE MISSED IT!
LUCKY FOR HIM IT WASN'T A STRAIGHT 'UN!

BRACKETT'S HAT LANDED ON THE WICKET . . .
ZAT!
?

HE'S OUT!
HE CAN'T BE, SURELY? HE WASN'T BOWLED! HIS HAT KNOCKED THE BAILS OFF.
HE'S OUR LAST MAN. IF HE'S OUT, THE INNINGS IS OVER — AND WE'VE LOST!

HOW CAN IT BE? THE BALL NEVER TOUCHED THE WICKET. MY HAT FELL ON IT.
OUT!

DIGGER RACED DOWN THE PITCH . . .
DON'T ARGUE, SPORT. THE LAWS SAY THAT IF, WHEN MAKING A STROKE, YOU BREAK THE WICKET WITH ANY PART OF YOUR CLOTHING, YOU'RE OUT!

DIGGER'S SNOOTY COUSIN CLARENCE MADE NO EFFORT TO HIDE HIS ILL-NATURED DELIGHT . . .
DIGGER'S COMING OFF — IT'S FINISHED — THEY'VE LOST!
WELL, UNCLE THEO, THAT'S THE END OF DIGGER'S SCHEME FOR A TEAM TO RIVAL MY COUNTY TEAM, SOUTHSHIRE. HIS FIRST TOURNAMENT MATCH— AND HIS LAST!

YOU'RE FORGETTING SOMETHING, CLARRY-MATE. THE QUALIFYING ROUND OF THE TOURNAMENT IS DECIDED HOME AND AWAY . . . WE'VE STILL GOT THE RETURN MATCH . . .
BUT, AS THE RUNS ARE CARRIED FORWARD TO THE SECOND LEG, WE START 47 RUNS BEHIND!

DIGGER'S LOYAL ABORIGINAL PAL JIM-JIM, WAS PUZZLED . . .
BOSS, WHY DIDN'T YOU TELL US ABOUT THE SECOND LEG? DO YOU REALLY THINK WE STAND ANY CHANCE AFTER WHAT HAPPENED TODAY?
WELL, COBBER, I FIGURED YOU LOT WOULD TRY ALL THE HARDER IF YOU THOUGHT YOU'D GOT JUST ONE CHANCE OF WINNING. NOW WE CAN ALL HAVE ANOTHER BASH IN THE RETURN GAME!
AND DIGGER'S SIDE WON THE RETURN— AND DEANSHIRE WAS FORMED!

NIPPER

NIPPER LAWRENCE, STAR OF BLACKPORT ROVERS, WAS SIGNING AUTOGRAPHS...
IT WAS A SPLENDID IDEA TO HAVE YOUNG LAWRENCE HERE ON AN AUTOGRAPH-SIGNING SESSION. IT'S EXCELLENT PUBLICITY FOR THE STORE!
← SPORTS GOODS
HE'S CERTAINLY ATTRACTING PLENTY OF ATTENTION FROM THE YOUNGER FANS!

OKAY, KIDS, THAT'S IT. I'LL HAVE TO STOP NOW... MY HAND IS ACHING TOO MUCH TO SIGN ANY MORE. I'LL SEE YOU ALL AT THE MATCH ON SATURDAY...
HEY, YOU HAVEN'T SIGNED MY BOOK YET...

I MUST GET YOUR AUTOGRAPH! I... OOOPS!
AAARGH!

UURGH... M-MY ANKLE... I'VE TWISTED IT... THANKS TO YOU!
SORRY, SORRY! I DIDN'T MEAN IT!

I KNOW YOU DIDN'T MEAN IT, LAD... BUT YOU CAN GIVE ME A HAND... THERE'S A CAR WAITING OUTSIDE FOR ME.
← SPORTS GOODS
I'D BETTER GET DOWN TO THE GROUND FOR SOME TREATMENT. IT'S THE BIG CUP GAME ON SATURDAY. I'VE GOT TO BE FIT FOR THAT!

THE YOUNG BOY HELPED NIPPER INTO THE CAR. AND THEN...
I DON'T USUALLY TRAVEL IN LUXURY LIKE THIS... BUT THE STORE PROVIDED THE CAR.
OKAY, MISTER LAWRENCE... I'LL JUST SHUT THE DOOR...

THEN IT HAPPENED! THE DOOR SLAMMED ON NIPPER'S FINGERS!
YEEE-AAAAARGH!

QUICK... DRIVE ON, CHUM... GET ME AWAY FROM THAT MENACE!
SORRY... I DIDN'T MEAN IT!
I DIDN'T GET HIS AUTOGRAPH...

IN THE BLACKPORT TREATMENT ROOM, TRAINER RON BAYLISS GOT TO WORK...
THERE... YOU'RE ALL FIXED UP. YOUR FINGERS ARE BADLY BRUISED... AND YOUR ANKLE'S GOT A SLIGHT STRAIN. BUT YOU SHOULD BE ALL RIGHT FOR THE MATCH, LAD!
PHEW, THAT'S A RELIEF!
SOMEONE TO SEE YOU, NIPPER...

THIS LAD SAYS YOU FORGOT TO SIGN HIS AUTOGRAPH BOOK!
EEEEK! IT'S HIM!

K-KEEP HIM AWAY... HE'S DANGEROUS!
NIPPER... LOOK OUT... THAT BOTTLE!

GGNGRGH!
SORRY... I DIDN'T MEAN IT!

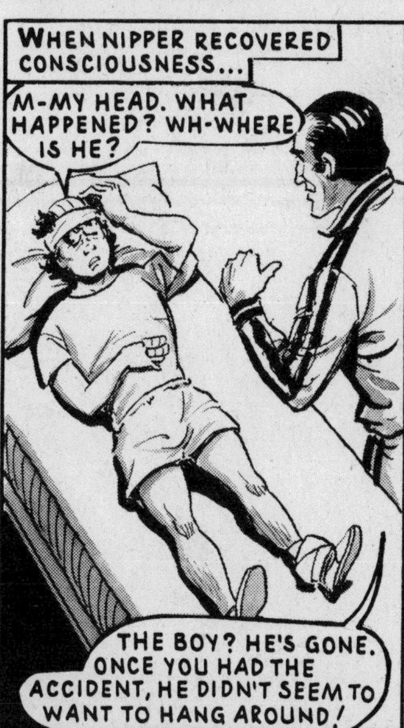
WHEN NIPPER RECOVERED CONSCIOUSNESS...
M-MY HEAD. WHAT HAPPENED? WH-WHERE IS HE?
THE BOY? HE'S GONE. ONCE YOU HAD THE ACCIDENT, HE DIDN'T SEEM TO WANT TO HANG AROUND!

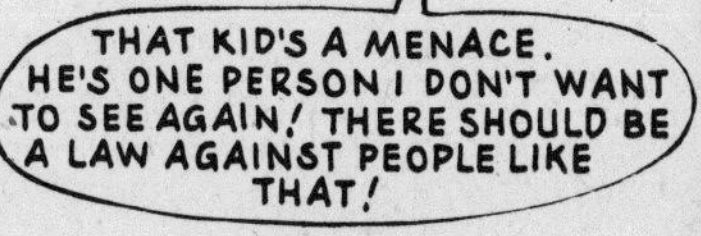
THAT KID'S A MENACE. HE'S ONE PERSON I DON'T WANT TO SEE AGAIN! THERE SHOULD BE A LAW AGAINST PEOPLE LIKE THAT!

NIPPER QUICKLY RECOVERED FROM HIS INJURIES AND ON MATCH DAY...
BLACKPORT! BLACKPORT! BLACKPORT!
GOOD LUCK, LADS!
GIVE US A GOAL, TODAY, NIPPER!

HE WAS SOON SHOWING FINE FORM...
GREAT HEADER, NIPPER!
THAT'S THE WAY TO PLAY!

BUT AS THE BLACKPORT STAR WENT TO GATHER THE BALL FOR A THROW-IN...
HELLO... IT'S ME AGAIN. I NEVER DID GET YOUR AUTOGRAPH!
AAARGH!

D-DON'T COME NEAR ME. YOU... URGH! MY HEAD!
SORRY... I DIDN'T MEAN IT!
RADIO

AFTER TREATMENT...
ARE YOU SURE YOU'RE GOING TO BE ALL RIGHT, NIPPER?
S-SURE. IT WAS ONLY A LITTLE BUMP. I'LL SURVIVE!
THIS IS RIDICULOUS! EVERY TIME I SEE THAT KID, SOMETHING HAPPENS TO ME!

BUT FROM THEN ON, NIPPER HAD A TERRIBLE GAME...
OH, NO...
WAY OVER THE BAR... USELESS!
IT WOULD HAVE BEEN EASIER TO SCORE!

EVENTUALLY, IT WAS NO SURPRISE WHEN HE WAS SUBSTITUTED.
8
OFF YOU COME, LAD... IT'S JUST NOT YOUR DAY.
IT WAS, UNTIL I SAW THAT KID!

I'LL GO AND TAKE AN EARLY BATH... I NEED ONE!
THAT MEANS YOU'LL HAVE TIME TO SIGN MY AUTOGRAPH BOOK...

G-GO AWAY! YOU... EEEEEEEERGH!
SORRY... I DIDN'T MEAN IT!

THE NEXT THING NIPPER KNEW... HE WAS RECOVERING CONSCIOUSNESS IN A HOSPITAL WARD...
UURGH... WH-WHAT HAPPENED?
YOU JUST HAD A LITTLE FALL. NOTHING SERIOUS. YOU'RE JUST IN FOR OBSERVATION. YOUR FANS ARE ALREADY SENDING YOU PRESENTS. THESE FLOWERS JUST ARRIVED... WITH THIS CARD...

IT... IT'S FROM HIM!
Sorry- I didn't mean it!

MAYBE HE'S NOT SUCH A BAD KID AFTER ALL. NEXT TIME I SEE HIM, I WILL GIVE HIM MY AUTOGRAPH! ONLY ONE OF THOSE ACCIDENTS WAS REALLY HIS FAULT.

THANKS FOR FORGIVING ME, NIPPER. CAN I HAVE YOUR AUTOGRAPH NOW?
SORRY... I DIDN'T MEAN IT!
AAAARGH!

BILLY DANE'S SPORTS QUIZ!

Billy Dane here, pals! If you think you've got a good sports knowledge, then it's about to be put to the test! Score two points for each correct answer, or part of an answer, then award yourself a medal as on page 117. Good luck!

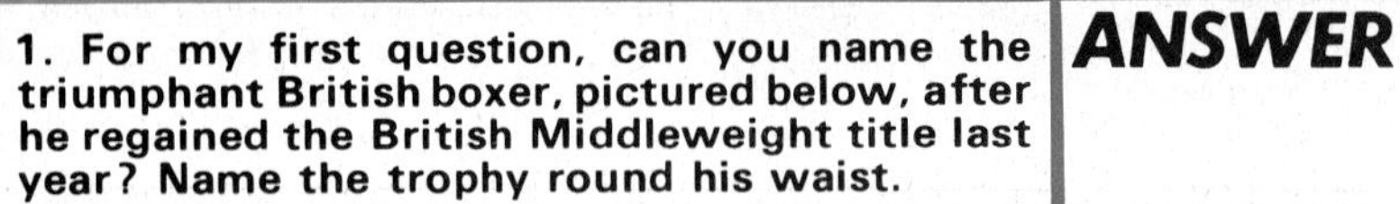

1. For my first question, can you name the triumphant British boxer, pictured below, after he regained the British Middleweight title last year? Name the trophy round his waist.

ANSWER

2. Attention, all soccer fans! Can you say which clubs play at the following grounds? (a) Dean Court; (b) Vetch Field; (c) Carrow Road; (d) Ayresome Park; (e) Turf Moor; (f) Portman Road. There's a total of twelve points to be won, for an all-correct answer.

ANSWER

3. Can you say if the following statements are true or false? (a) India have never beaten Australia in a cricket Test match series. (b) The 1979 World Motor Racing Formula One Champion drove a Ferrari. (c) Archery became an Olympic sport for the first time in 1972. (d) "Riposte" is a term used in Judo.

ANSWER

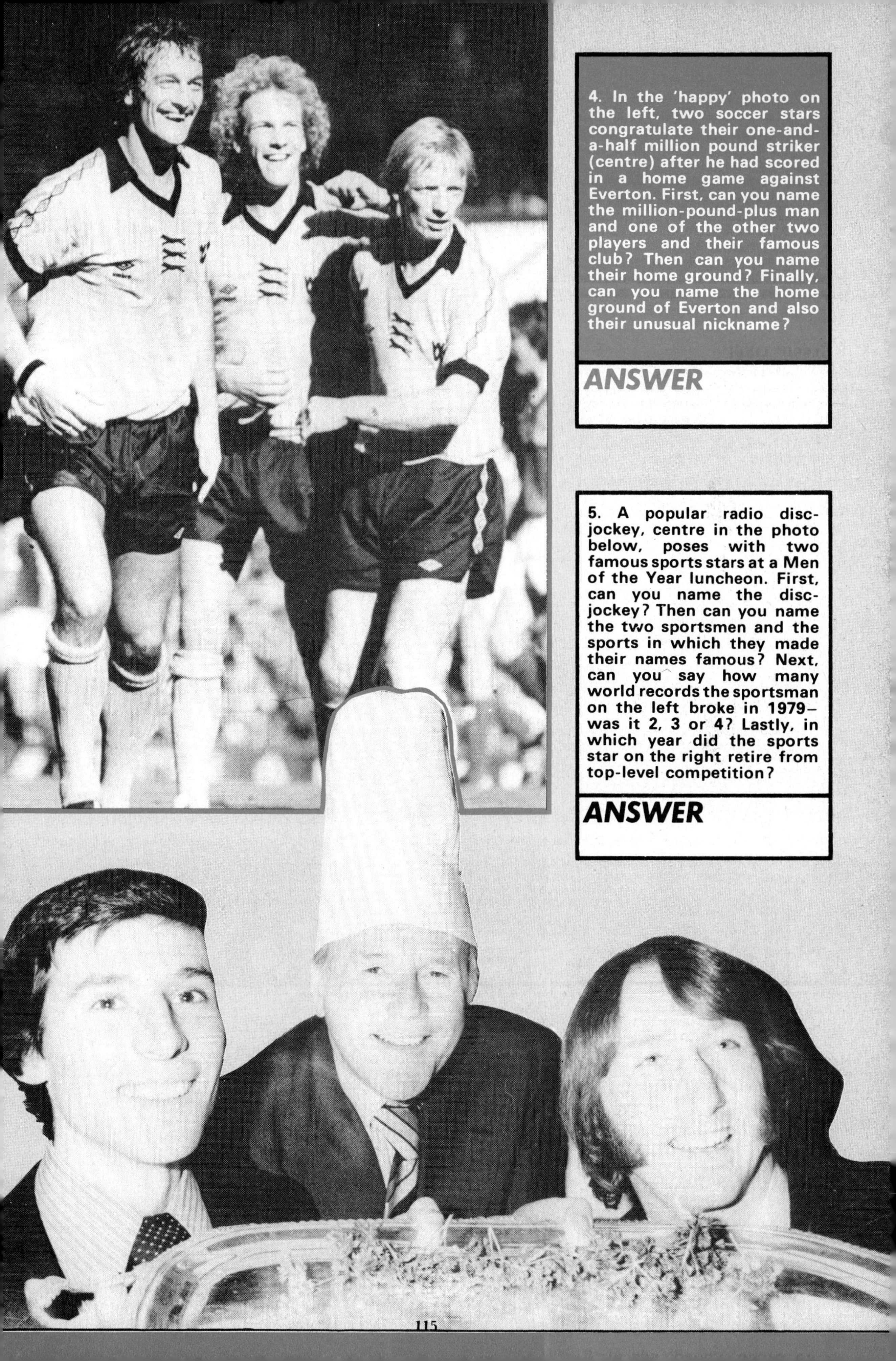

4. In the 'happy' photo on the left, two soccer stars congratulate their one-and-a-half million pound striker (centre) after he had scored in a home game against Everton. First, can you name the million-pound-plus man and one of the other two players and their famous club? Then can you name their home ground? Finally, can you name the home ground of Everton and also their unusual nickname?

ANSWER

5. A popular radio disc-jockey, centre in the photo below, poses with two famous sports stars at a Men of the Year luncheon. First, can you name the disc-jockey? Then can you name the two sportsmen and the sports in which they made their names famous? Next, can you say how many world records the sportsman on the left broke in 1979–was it 2, 3 or 4? Lastly, in which year did the sports star on the right retire from top-level competition?

ANSWER

6. Try this puzzle question. Starting at the top of the circle on the left and working clockwise, can you take one letter from each segment in turn, to spell the seven-letter name of a soccer club that is followed by the word 'City'? Then in the same way, repeat the process twice more, to find two more seven-letter 'City' football clubs.

ANSWER

7. Now can you say with which sports you would associate the following past and present sports stars? (a) Timo Makinen; (b) Barry John; (c) Sharron Davies; (d) John Lowe, (e) John Charles; (f) Nelson Piquet. Think carefully now, pals and have a guess if you're not sure.

ANSWER

8. A famous cricketer proudly holds the International Batsman of the Year trophy he won at the Oval. Name him, the county he's played for and the country he's skippered.

ANSWER

9. The super soccer photo, above, was taken at a London 'derby' game at the ground of the player on the right's club. Name the sides taking part and the players shown. Then name the countries they've played for and the home grounds of their clubs at the time.

ANSWER

ANSWERS

(1) Kevin Finnegan. The Lonsdale Belt. (2) a. Bournemouth. b. Swansea City. c. Norwich City. d. Middlesbrough. e. Burnley. f. Ipswich Town. (3) a. False. India beat Australia for the first time in a Test series in 1979. b. True. c. False. Archery was REINTRODUCED to the Olympics in 1972, for the first time since 1920. d. False. Riposte is a fencing term. (4) Andy Gray. The other two players are Kenny Hibbitt (left) and Willie Carr. Wolverhampton Wanderers. Molineux. Goodison Park. The Toffeemen. (5) Jimmy Young. Sebastian Coe (Athletics), left, and J. P. R. Williams (Rugby Union). Coe broke 3 world records. 1979. (6) Norwich City; Lincoln City; Bristol City. (7) a. Rallying or Powerboat Racing. b. Rugby Union. c. Swimming. d. Darts. e. Football. f. Motor racing. (8) Clive Lloyd. Lancashire. West Indies. (9) Arsenal v Crystal Palace. Liam Brady (left) and Gerry Francis. Brady's played for Eire and Francis for England. Arsenal play at Highbury and Crystal Palace at Selhurst Park.

How did you score, chums? The points total for each medal is shown beneath them. But please don't send your medals to us—this is a competition for you to enjoy at home. I hope you all got a gold medal!

70–90 points

48–68 points

26–46 points

THE RICHEST SINGLE SHOT IN GOLF

At the start of the 1979 World Match Play tournament, brilliant Japanese golfer Isao Aoki little realised that he would win a prize worth £25,000 more than the cheque the winner of the competition would receive! As often happens in top golf tournaments, for any golfer lucky enough to get a hole-in-one, a special prize was set aside—and it was fantastic! To be precise—a furnished apartment overlooking Gleneagles golf course, worth £55,000! Let's follow Aoki, as he hits his drive towards the second green, right.

Aoki's shot soared high in the air and the ball bounced once, before going straight in the hole, to the delight of the Japanese and his partner David Graham, left.

After his amazing shot, Aoki rushed to the green to get the ball out of the hole and kiss it, left. Then, below, he acknowledges the cheers of the crowd. And in the photo at the foot of the page, you can see his magnificent prize. It was the first hole-in-one in the 16-year history of the tournament—and the richest single shot in golf!

FILE OF FAME

SWIMMING
ATHLETICS
BADMINTON
TENNIS
GOLF

THEN, THE FLYERS' WINGER MADE A SUPERB PASS...
WOW! THAT'S STRAIGHT AND TRUE!
AND IT'S FOUND THEIR CENTREMAN, ROCKY LISTON!

OPPOSING PLAYERS OF HORONTO HAWKS QUICKLY ROUNDED ON ROCKY...
NOW COME ON, LISTON... DON'T CHICKEN OUT! USE THAT NATURAL SPEED OF YOURS ... TAKE THE PUCK THROUGH THEM! FAIL ME AND I'LL NEVER FORGIVE YOU!

THE HAWKS' GOALKEEPER WAS SURPRISED, TOO!
GOAL!
YIKES!
A BRILLIANT MOVE BY ROCKY!
AS FREQUENTLY HAPPENS IN THE FAST AND FRANTIC GAME OF ICE HOCKEY, ROCKY WAS SUBSTITUTED...
PLEASED WITH ME, BOSS? I RECKON THAT WAS ONE OF THE BEST GOALS I'VE EVER SCORED!
PLEASED? YOU ASK ME IF I'M PLEASED—?
NITWIT! HOW CAN I BE PLEASED WITH A TEAM WHO ARE ALWAYS GIVING ME SCRAMBLED NERVES? I HAVE TO PUSH AND DRIVE YOU TO VICTORIES ...WHY ELSE DO YOU THINK I SHOUT SO MUCH?
HORONTO HAWKS TRIED HARD...
GO IT, HAWKS!
YAHOO! THIS LOOKS LIKE A CHANCE FOR THEM!
BUT FENTOWN FLYERS HAD A GREAT GOAL-KEEPER IN BIG BILL BIXBY!
YOU LEAVE MY GOAL ALONE!
A FANTASTIC CATCH!
THERE AREN'T MANY SHOTS THAT GET PAST BIG BILL!
THE FLYERS WERE QUICK TO RE-ATTACK...
HURRY, HURRY... YOU'VE GOT ONLY A FEW SECONDS LEFT!
HEAR THAT? THE BOSS WANTS US TO SCORE AGAIN...

...SO LET'S MAKE HIM HAPPY!
THANKS, CHUCK! YOURS, MAX...
I'VE GOT IT, LUKE!
GOAL!

THE FANS SHOWED THEIR APPRECIATION...
YOU'RE A SUPER TEAM, FLYERS!
HURRAH!
THIS HAS BEEN OUR BIGGEST WIN THIS SEASON ... SIX GOALS TO NIL!
LET'S HOPE THE BOSS IS FULL OF CHEER... FOR ONCE!

BUT IN THE DRESSING-ROOM...
DON'T BE SO READY TO CONGRATULATE YOURSELVES...THERE'S STILL LOTS OF IMPROVEMENTS TO BE MADE! IN FACT, I WAS VERY DISAPPOINTED...
WITH A SIX-NIL WIN?
ENOUGH'S ENOUGH, FELLAS! I'M GOING TO TELL HIM...

ROCKY LISTON HAD PLENTY TO SAY...

NOW YOU LISTEN TO US, BOSS... WE'RE NOT TAKING ANY MORE OF YOUR BAWLING AND COMPLAINING! MAYBE YOU HAVE HELPED BRING SUCCESS TO THE TEAM...BUT OUR LIVES ARE A MISERY! EITHER YOU CUT IT OUT...OR WE ALL LEAVE THE FLYERS!

SO THAT'S HOW YOU FEEL, EH?
RIGHT! ROCKY COULDN'T HAVE SAID IT BETTER!
YOU CHANGE YOUR WAYS... OR WE GO!

OKAY...I GET THE PICTURE. FROM NOW ON, I'LL BE A DIFFERENT MANAGER.
GREAT! THAT'S JUST WHAT WE WANT!
DON'T FORGET ...YOU'RE NOT TO LOSE YOUR TEMPER AGAIN!

BUT THE MANAGER NEEDED NO REMINDING...
WOULD YOU GUYS KINDLY DO THESE FITNESS EXERCISES AS INSTRUCTED BY ME? I'M SORRY IF THEY'RE BORING...
WE'LL DO THE EXERCISES AS WE ALWAYS HAVE DONE, BOSS...

GOSH, IT SURE IS STRANGE TO SEE HIM SO NICE AND POLITE ... IT'S MOST UNNATURAL!
IT'S ALSO A LOT MORE **PEACEFUL** THAN BEFORE ...WHICH IS HOW I PREFER THINGS!

AND AT A MEETING TO DISCUSS THE NEXT MATCH...
GUS ISN'T HERE. INSTEAD HE'S LEFT A NOTE...
"REALISING THE TEAM'S CONFIDENCE, I DON'T BELIEVE THERE'S ANY NEED FOR PEP-TALKS. I SUGGEST YOU TAKE THE DAY OFF TO RELAX..."
GREAT IDEA!

THE TEAM WENT FOR A PICNIC...
LIFE IS A WHOLE LOT BETTER SINCE GUS CHANGED!
YET IN A FUNNY KIND OF WAY, I MISS THAT AWFUL BAWLING VOICE OF HIS...

WATTAWA RANGERS WERE THE NEXT OPPONENTS...
AN AWAY GAME FOR US... BUT WE BEAT THE RANGERS THE LAST TIME WE MET!
I'VE NEVER FELT SO RELAXED FOR A GAME!
FF
FF

GOOD LUCK, MEN!
THANKS, BOSS!
WE'VE NEVER SEEN GUS LOOKING SO RELAXED AND QUIET, EITHER... THOUGH I STILL CAN'T GET USED TO IT!

A 'FACE-OFF' STARTED THE GAME, WITH THE REFEREE DROPPING THE PUCK BETWEEN THE TWO OPPOSING CENTREMEN...
GREAT MOVING, ROCKY LISTON! HE'S GOT THE PUCK FIRST!
THE FLYERS ARE ABOUT TO TAKE OFF!
15

BUT ALMOST IMMEDIATELY, THINGS BEGAN TO GO WRONG...
HAW! LISTON IS TOO SPEEDY FOR HIS OWN GOOD... HE'S LOST CONTROL OF THE PUCK!
A RANGER HAS SNATCHED IT AWAY!

WATTAWA RANGERS POWERED INTO SUDDEN ATTACK...
OHH, LOOK AT THAT SUPERB ACCURATE PASSING!
THEY'RE RUNNING RINGS ROUND THE FLYERS!

AND BEFORE BIG BILL BIXBY KNEW IT...
GOAL! YAHOO! THE RANGERS HAVE SCORED!
LIVEN UP, FLYERS! YOU'RE IN A DAZE!

ROCKY LISTON GLANCED OVER AT HIS MANAGER...
GUS IS JUST SITTING THERE... AND SAYING NOTHING. BEFORE, HE WOULD HAVE BAWLED OUR EARS OFF FOR ALLOWING THAT GOAL...

FENTON FLYERS MADE MORE MISTAKES... DISASTROUS ONES...
AAAGH! I'VE BEEN HOOKED...
S-SORRY... IT WAS AN ACCIDENT!
OH, NO! ACCIDENT OR NOT, HANK... YOU TRIPPED THE RANGERS PLAYER WHEN HE WAS IN A SCORING POSITION!

AS ROCKY GUESSED, A PENALTY WAS AWARDED... AND...
HOORAY! RANGERS NOW LEAD, TWO-NIL!
THE FLYERS ARE USELESS!

STILL, GUS BREWER SAID NOTHING...

THEN, AT THE END OF THE FIRST TWENTY-MINUTE PERIOD...
WE'RE NOT PLAYING WITH ANY GUMPTION... OUR WILL TO WIN ISN'T THERE. DO YOU KNOW WHY, FELLAS ?
YES, ROCKY...
AND WE KNOW WHAT WE'VE GOT TO DO...
FF

THE ICE HOCKEY FANS HAD NEVER WITNESSED SUCH AN AMAZING SCENE...
PLEASE, BOSS... TREAT US LIKE YOU USED TO !
DON'T BE SO QUIET... WE CAN'T STAND IT !
LOSE YOUR TEMPER WITH US...
LET US HEAR THAT BAWLING VOICE AGAIN !
WE CAN'T PLAY WITHOUT IT !

SO YOU DON'T LIKE ME AS A QUIET MANAGER... YOU MISS ME SHOUTING AT YOU ? YES, I THOUGHT THIS MIGHT HAPPEN. FOR SOME DAYS, I'VE HELD BACK MY TEMPER... AND NOW YOU'RE ASKING ME TO LOSE IT ?

I'VE GOOD REASON TO ! YOU'RE THE MOST APPALLING ICE HOCKEY TEAM IN THE WORLD ! I'M ASHAMED TO BE YOUR MANAGER... BUT YOU WON'T GIVE UP BECAUSE YOU'RE TWO GOALS DOWN ! YOU'LL FIGHT BACK AND **WIN!**
LISTEN TO THAT ...PURE MUSIC!
I'M FEELING BETTER ALREADY!
FF

AND DRIVEN ON BY THEIR FIERY MANAGER, THE FENTOWN FLYERS WON THAT MATCH. NEVER AGAIN DID THEY PROTEST ABOUT GUS BREWER'S TEMPER... AFTER ALL, IT WAS SOMETHING THEY ***NEEDED!***
FENTON FLYERS

FOILED BY THE 'KEEPER!